PRIVATE
OF A
MLA
SUSPENDED

To Eileen,

Thanks for coming tonight,

Garbhan Downey

Garbhan Downey

Cover illustration by John McCloskey

© Copyright Stormount Books, October 2004
Tel: 079 1035 8140
Email: info@stormountbooks.com

For Una, who bought me cufflinks for the book launch before a word was written.

Previous Books by the Author

Just One Big Party: A Fan's-Eye View of the 1994 World Cup, published by Forum Books, 1994

Creggan: More Than A History (with Michael McGuinness), published by Guildhall Press, 2000

About the Author

Garbhan Downey's descent into journalism began when he was appointed editor of the student newspaper at University College Galway. Any thoughts he had of pursuing an alternative career in politics disappeared after a year in Dublin with the Union of Students in Ireland. Instead, he returned to his native city and began writing for the *Derry Journal*. He followed this with a stretch as a staff reporter with the *Londonderry Sentinel*, before moving on to the *Irish News* to become the paper's Derry correspondent. Downey then spent several years with the BBC in Derry and Belfast before completing a three-year stint as editor of the *Derry News*. He is married to Una and has two children.

Acknowledgements

Working in newspapers, you get used to the idea that scores of people contribute to the finished product. But it was still quite an eye-opener to discover that books require every bit as much of a team effort and that the guy with his name on the cover is only the front man.

First and foremost, I'd like to thank my family for their patience and support. Una, the love of my life, spent her summer reading, re-reading, proofreading, advising and taking out bad jokes, and I cannot thank her enough for it. Gerry, my father, studied the early drafts of the book and advised how I might rectify things. I did my best to listen to his excellent counsel and would stress that any failings are mine. My mother Aine and mother-in-law Cecilia both gave me tremendous encouragement to make the leap from journalism into full-time writing, and I hope that one day I justify their faith in me. Likewise, I can't omit my late brother Ronan who tried to tell me many times that life is not all about punching a work-clock. Throughout the process, my son Fiachra (five) provided much-needed escape in the form of nightly penalty competitions in the garden, while Bronagh (20 months) ensured I stuck rigidly to my early-morning start time.

This publication, of course, would not have been possible without the efforts of all at Stormount Books. They proved themselves to be meticulous editors and first-class arbiters on everything from grammar to taste and decency.

John, who designed the cover, did a masterful job. Indeed, his illustration was all the more outstanding given the fact that he got no notice and any input from me was muddled and confusing. No doubt he will make up for it by knocking me onto my ear at our Monday night indoor football sessions, just as he's been doing for the past 15 years.

This book, I would stress, is a work of fiction, but my experience in the media proved invaluable in writing it. In particular, I'd like to thank Colm for facilitating the three-year case study at the *Derry News* that preceded this book. I learnt more about politics there than if I were to spend the rest of my life at Stormont. Needless to say, I also borrowed mercilessly from others: Mickey O, another of the football crew, has contributed his share of one-liners; and C.T. gave me all the gen on how mileometers are docked.

I got a lot of advice when I decided to try my hand at full-time writing – some good, some a little too direct for my liking – but none more inspiring than that I got from Dave, yet another Monday night indoor star. It meant a lot.

Thanks also to Aoife for her invaluable technical support and Sadie for taking good care of F&B while their daddy sweated in the attic.

There are also a number of other people, you'll understand, who mightn't thank me for thanking them in this particular book. I just want them to know I really appreciate their input.

Prologue

Shay Gallagher was always going to be a politician. He'd no choice in the matter; it was in his blood. It's like being an alcoholic, only there's no 12-step programme.

Personally, I'll take the drink over politics any day — you tend to damage fewer people. Though maybe that's not entirely fair in Shay's case. He's still young enough and naïve enough to make a difference. That's why we got him to run, 'King Size' Barkley and myself. That and we were bored and wanted a laugh.

The first time I met Shay was 15 years ago, when he landed in Dublin straight out of school. I'd already spent five years there studying law and was having trouble finding an apprenticeship until Shay's uncle, Seamus Senior, stepped in and fixed me up through some of his party connections. Old Seamus was a neighbour of mine from north Derry and the independent chairman of Dunavady Council.

The payback was Young Shay, who was forsaking the bright lights of Derry city for First Arts at UCD. "For Christ's sake, keep a tight eye on him, Tommy," the uncle had said. "He's always been a big innocent sort of a bastard."

Jesus, there was an understatement. If you'd shone a light into Shay's ear, the only thing that would have stopped it shooting out the other side was the big wooden spike pinning his head onto his neck.

But a deal is a deal, so I groomed him as carefully as I could during the two years we shared a flat. And in fairness, Shay was an able pupil. By the time I moved back to Dunavady to set up shop, he was well on his way to a first class honours in late night drinking and picking up women.

But try as I might, I just couldn't knock any damned cynicism into him. And of course, I couldn't shake the damned politics out of him either — he was too idealistic. Shay's just one of these guys who can't stop himself from being interested in people. No money in it, I always tell him. But he's an addict.

It wasn't hard to persuade Shay to come and work here, once he'd qualified as a teacher. Dunavady is a very beautiful little town — full of smart and friendly country people, and the hinterland features some of the most spectacular scenery on the island. Most people who come here for any length of time tend to stay. Shay has been here almost a decade now himself, and we've long adopted him as one of our own.

When Uncle Seamus got Shay his start at St Fiachra's, he never told him that he was also the political heir apparent. Everybody else either knew it or assumed it. But Shay only found out when the oul' fella keeled over three years ago during a GAA Vets tournament in Greysteel, at the age of 64. And less than a month later, Shay was a town councillor.

Of course, he never should have been elected to Stormont, or 'Stormount' as they call it here. Fianna Fáil had only wanted to test the temperature north of the border and had asked me to get a candidate to run, on the quiet, as a 'non-party' nationalist. Shay was already an independent councillor, so he was a perfect choice. And it was only supposed to be a bit of fun.

Then, fuck me, if the world didn't cave in out in Dunavady, and Shay went and got himself voted in as a real live Member of the Legislative Assembly for North Derry.

I can't see him hacking it for too long; he's way out of his depth. Though, to be honest, he's a lot less dangerous sticking with politics and screwing the public, than teaching French to 18-year-old girls...

So, anyhow, I put it to Shay that he should keep a record of his time as an MLA. And, as an election present, I bought him a big leather-bound five-year diary. I thought he could keep it in his constituency office to log all the major political developments — and maybe include any relevant newspaper cuttings.

But typical of the big donkey, he kept it at home so he could add in his private memoirs as well. And now, given everything that's happened since last November, he's begged me to take the diary back and stash it in my safe. He even told me, God be good to him, that I was the only person on earth he could trust not to read it.

As the uncle said, he's always been a big innocent sort of a bastard.

Tommy 'Bowtie' McGinlay
October 2004

NOVEMBER 2003

It's never easy to justify reading someone else's diary — even if you are their lawyer. People are inclined to think you're a nosey bollix. The exception, of course, is when it's a matter of vital public interest — such as murder, mayhem, corruption or wholesale debauchery. So I think we're probably covered then.

It did require a little editing. For instance, I've left out all his dental appointments, visits to his mother, and his weekly promises to go off the drink. But I've included all the important bits. And I've also provided a few explanatory notes at the start and end of each month for the virgin reader, which I trust you are.

It all started off so well too. A 40-grand salary — and no work on the horizon for the guts of a year. What the hell could possibly go wrong?

•••••••

Saturday, November 29

Never, ever make a promise in a pub. Not, Dear Diary, that I made any last night; we were all far too shot through with good booze for that.

The celebrations began in earnest at 10.00pm — after the returning officer refused to do a fifth recount. Take your oil, Blunt, you BIGOT!

Then you had the speeches. I'd like to thank: the Loyalist Action Group for bumping off the Shinners' front-runner after nominations closed; Messrs Benson & Hedges for doing a similar job on the SDLP's main attraction; the Derry Standard for exposing my fellow independent as a convicted pervert; and the PSNI for slapping me in handcuffs at the polling station and doubling my profile on election day. Oh, and did I mention my principal, Fr Know-All Giddens? Sit on this, you fat old git – and you can beat your Head of Languages job up your hole.

And no, you're right, Diary, I said none of the above – but if I'm going to be truthful here, that's pretty much what I was thinking.

No, instead, I paid tribute to Tommy Bowtie, my self-appointed election agent, for all his fine work. (Three cheers for Tommy – could somebody wake him from underneath that pile of coats? Sorry, he is that pile of coats...) I then thanked Barry 'King Size' Barkley and my other financial backers; 'Chiselling' Phil Stevenson and my strategists; Susie 'Short Shorts' and the team who put up my election posters; and, of course, the special committee who took down everyone else's.

I also congratulated my opponents on their fairness and decency on the hustings – and particularly whoever leaked it to the Daily Mirror that I get through more skirt than Dolce & Gabbana. I've the clipping framed and up on the wall.

A special mention, too, went to William Coyle, bookmaker of this parish, who gatecrashed the party to present me with a cheque for £1,000. A most gallant gesture, considering not a month ago, he laughed me out of the shop for sticking a tenner on myself at 100-1. William, however, then left the do quickly, when someone suggested that he might be buying drink.

Moving on to the press — the Derry Standard actually printed my press statements and gave me quite generous coverage for an independent, so I thanked them. But the BBC and UTV reckon that if you're not a member of the Big Four, you have no business in politics. So when you come looking for soft-profile interviews next week, you can go fart in a large jar. (Though again, of course, I didn't say that last bit.)

You have to throw in a couple of jokes as well. So I thanked both Alan Clark and Dana for their inspiration – Alan for showing me the real reason good-looking men get into politics, and Dana for convincing me that no-one was going to hold it against me that I'm a lousy singer.

Then, last but not least, of course, I expressed my great appreciation to those two very special ladies who are so important in my life – they both know who they are. (Damned if I do but I suppose one of them's gotta be my mother.) Anyway, this drew the biggest applause of the night, so I quit while I was ahead, and went back to the bar to buy another round for the troops.

As the night wore on, sporadic singing erupted, ranging from The Red Flag (taxi for McCann) to Four Green Fields (go party with the Provies upstairs) to The Town I Loved So Well (who let John Hume in?).

After that, someone had the bright idea of organising a limerick competition featuring the names of other candidates. And the tone rapidly degenerated.

Actually, if I'm to be honest, even that was going rightly – apart from a few dubious rhymes with Nelis and Rankin. But then Tommy Bowtie got his second wind and began reciting one about the guy I beat to the sixth seat – the DUP's Tony Blunt. So the staff at The Jack Kennedy Inn closed the bar and ordered us up a fleet of hacks. Quite right too.

But back to my opening point, Diary. Bad and all as I was last night, as far as I recall, I didn't make any promises in the bar. Sadly, that ship sailed eight weeks ago, when a gulpin with too much stout on board announced that if that dog-lover goes up as a candidate, I'll run myself. And when Tommy Bowtie played back the tape the following day, it sounded exactly like me. Thus explaining the pickle I'm now in…

The taxis arrived, and Great White Hope Number Two, a complete pro, oxtered me to the car, where she kissed me goodnight. I thanked her profusely and told her I'd add five gold stars to her chart when I got home.

The taxi then shot off like a bullet to avoid a bunch of stragglers wanting to share the fare. Indeed, I was just about to commend the driver on his evasion skills when he braked suddenly to avoid a drunken jaywalker, and unfortunately, he upset more than the applecart. And before you could say Not Again, Mucker, Shay Gallagher, the newly elected representative for North Derry, whirled his head to the side and sprayed the back seat with 15 pints of Guinness and two wee brandies.

Must have been all those canapés.

Sunday, November 30

I didn't realise until I read this morning's papers that last week was the fortieth anniversary of Jack Kennedy's assassination. Though this is hardly surprising, considering I spent all day yesterday convinced that I also had been shot in the back of the head.

The last time I was at the doctor, he was very impressed by the fact that I never drink at all during the week. So he asked me how many units I drank at the weekends.

"About 30 pints," I replied.

"Thirty pints!" he yelled. "Have you any idea how much that is?"

"Guts of 80 quid," I told him.

Anyhow, Friday night's taxi driver, so Great White Hope Number Two tells me, had to be tipped pretty handsomely never to have seen me. Typical Shinner – if I'd been Gerry Adams, he'd have siphoned up the carrots and sold them off in bags.

The Sunday papers have largely been kind to me, with lots of "confounding the experts", "breaking the traditional moulds", and one particularly memorable "good-looking young bachelor". (Pretty picture by-line, must drop her a thank-you card.)

My favourite was the piece in the Sunday Business Post, a Dublin paper, which, unusually, doesn't think all northern nationalists come equipped with balaclavas and IRA tattoos. It'll give me a decent start for my clippings collection:

GALLAGHER RAGES AGAINST THE MACHINES
By Michael Harrison

The new independent MLA for North Derry, Shay Gallagher, yesterday promised to challenge the "comfortable complicity" which allows the four main parties in the North to perpetuate stagnant politics.

The 33-year-old French teacher – who has never been in Stormont and visits Belfast "only at the point of a gun" – was the last of the 108 MLAs to be elected on Friday night, after he saw off the challenge of the DUP's Tony Blunt for the final seat.

Protocol means that Gallagher will have to take an immediate sabbatical from his job at St Fiachra's Grammar School in Dunavady; despite the fact the Assembly is unlikely to sit until after the European elections next June at the earliest. And it is an anomaly the new MLA himself describes as "100 percent daft".

"Jesus, I thought teachers had it handy," Gallagher added.

"From Monday, I will be getting paid twice as much for sitting on my backside and staring out the window, as I do for working a 35-hour week. I haven't had this much fun since the Foyle Trust advertised for trainee gynaecologists.

"Seriously though, the main players have to start shaking themselves quickly. If we don't get the structures up again soon, our researchers will all have blinded themselves on the free internet porn."

Unknown

For the past three years, Gallagher has been sitting as an independent on Dunavady Council. He was co-opted into that post "reluctantly" on the death of his uncle Seamus (Shay) Gallagher Senior, who had also served in the Senate as a Fianna Fáil appointee.

But Shay Junior never intended to go any further in politics. Then, so legend has it, he got sight of the list of nominations for North Derry, drank himself into a depression, and woke up a candidate.

"Lies, all lies," he laughed good-humouredly. "I actually signed the papers the following day – when they threatened me with the negatives."

Despite being well known in the North Derry constituency, Gallagher, who still lives in his native Derry city, had not been expected to feature in the final six.

Sinn Féin had been strongly tipped to up their representation from one to three – they were targeting an SDLP seat and that of the independent MLA Brian 'Collie' Colloway. But the republicans' decision to run only three candidates blew up in their faces when their expected poll-topper, John 'Stumpy' O'Rourke, was murdered by loyalists, and they couldn't get another name on the ballot.

Then, ten days before the election, there was disaster too for the SDLP, when their main vote-puller, Peadar Naughton, dropped dead from a heart attack. And just four days before polling, Brian Colloway was forced to withdraw from the race after a series of damaging allegations in the local press.

This left the way clear for Gallagher to pick off the fourth nationalist seat. And he easily saw off the DUP, who realistically were always going to be 500 votes shy of a second quota.

The final returns in North Derry saw two Sinn Féin members elected (+1), one SDLP (-2), one UUP (no change), one DUP (no change), and one independent.

Great White Hope Number Two had read the report in the Business Post, and phoned to ask just exactly what is the difference between sitting on my arse looking out the window all day and teaching. Informed her she'd just lost herself three gold stars and that GWH Number One had told me how well I looked in the Sunday Life – and was shooting back up the table.

GWH Number One actually called over to tell me this in person, and is still in the shower, but Number Two isn't to know that.

Also, a spitting-mad Brian Colloway rang to say he had never been called 'Collie' in his life and that a solicitor's letter was in the post. Not going to happen, Brian. The conviction's there and on the record. Not my fault your career went into a tailspin.

Have to cut it there for today, Diary. Radio Ulster have asked me to do Seven Days from Radio Foyle and give some independent thinking on whether the Shinners and the Dups will ever get to talking. Me, Martin, Gregory – and some independent unionist girl from Omagh who's just been elected.

Was tempted to tell the Beeb to go whistle up a rope, but it's not everyday you get a chance to breathe last night's beer over the town's two best-known teetotallers.

Pity I didn't eat a curry before I went to bed.

•••••••

That Gallagher is one cheeky bastard. I know I'm not the most debonair chap in the world but a "pile of coats"? Just because he's a damn clotheshorse. Four weans and a wife who won't iron will soon knock that out of him.

Anyhow. Stumpy's killing was dreadful and the start of a series of events that would have grim consequences for all of us. Shay should have known better than to crack jokes about it, particularly in a diary. With the Shinners down to two candidates, the Stoops had a good chance to save a seat, but then old Peadar cowped over. And from that minute, I knew the seat was ours.

There was no way I was going to allow Collie Colloway to get re-elected. I'd actually defended him myself. He was only 19 at the time, and as far as I recall, we were instructed in court to refer to it as "non-consensual congress with a non-human partner". His father paid dear to keep it out of the papers. And normally, you'd respect their privacy. But Collie had got way above himself with his seat in Stormount, so I felt I'd a moral duty to expose him to public ridicule. That was achieved by sending the chairman of the SDLP's Dunavady Executive an anonymous copy of Collie's charge sheet while another went off to the Shinners' North Derry boss Chris Caddle. I don't know who leaked it to the *Standard* in the end — probably both of them.

The next trick was to raise Shay's profile, which we did in various ways — including getting him arrested. The BBC and UTV give candidates no profile whatsoever on Election Day unless it's of specific news interest, which of course Shay's arrest was. It was so easy done, too. I gave him my driving licence instead of his own as he went in to vote first thing in the morning — and then got our in-house polling clerk to cry "personation" when he handed over his ID. I even managed to get a freelance cameraman to film him being clapped in irons and frogmarched into a police jeep — and the clip made every TV bulletin of the day. That, combined with the fact that the police didn't apologise until late in the afternoon, allowed me to go on news programme after news programme and complain about the harassment of ordinary decent nationalists.

Shay, naturally, knew damn all about the plan — he'd only have blown it.

DECEMBER 2003

Our chief concern once we'd got Shay in the door was keeping him there. We always knew he was going to try and bail on us. He's a total flake — just like his old uncle, God rest him.

But King Size Barkley wasn't going to let Shay go without a fight. King Size was chairman of the Dunavady Improvement Agency, which was bidding for a hefty slice of Blair's £2 billion investment package. And he also owned a pile of land around the town, which he wanted zoned for development. No, Shay was far, far too useful.

Happily, however, Shay is always open to reasonable argument. And he's also not much of a boat-rocker, so if you present him with a done deal, he tends not to shout too much. So we were able to sort out a few teething problems without undue pain.

Handling him long-term was a different proposition altogether, however. King Size and I met up with Fr Know-All to discuss it, and we eventually agreed that the only way to shackle him properly was to get him married off. I'm not wild about matchmaking myself, but Fr K assures us it's a custom as old as time itself.

●●●●●●●

Monday, December 1

I suppose the best thing I can say about the Seven Days programme was that at least Martin was there to stop me getting a total pasting.

"Will the DUP and Sinn Féin sit down and talk?" asked that nice presenter Mark Carruthers.

Of course they will, I said. Sure, aren't they already sitting round this table like two horny youngsters in the back seats, just dying to get stuck in?

Wrong simile. Or is it metaphor? I can never remember. Not that it matters anyway, because the big guns were already out and shooting holes in it.

I don't think I got my neb in more than three times after that.

And one of those was when Gregory asked me what subject I taught. "French," I said proudly.

"Certainly wasn't dental hygiene, anyway," he retorted. Smart git.

Got chatting in the Radio Foyle kitchen afterwards to the independent unionist MLA for East Tyrone, and quite a tidy little package she is too. About 30 I'd reckon, no rings that would worry you, fiery red hair, sea-green eyes and a little tight waist; all beautifully set off by this killer black minidress that definitely ruled her out of Big Ian's camp.

"I didn't catch your name," I said.

"Sue McEwan," she replied, though a bit curt for my liking.

"As in the beer?" I asked.

"A subject obviously very dear to your heart," she said. "And you're Shay Gallagher. As in the guy that every mother in Derry and Tyrone warns her daughter about."

"Jesus," I said, "not Tyrone as well. I should never have gone to that All-Ireland final…"

That got a small smile, so I pressed on with my serious side.

"So, Sue, are you pro or anti-agreement?"

"I'm a soft no."

"Is that a real no – or secretly yes, but just no enough to get elected?"

"No, it's a real no," she sniffed. "Some of us are actually principled enough to hold positions."

Now there are a few positions Sue could hold for me, but this was not the time. So instead, I suggested that she could be my Assembly pair, should we ever get there. And surprisingly, she said it wasn't a bad idea.

I think I'm smitten.

Tuesday, December 2

The problem with not doing any proper work is that it is sticking a pin in my no-drinking-on-school-nights rule. Last night saw another heroic session down in Dunavady's Castle Inn. Indeed, a lesser man than me could get to like the stuff. So, Diary, I'm entrusting you to keep tabs on me: 28 units, no cigarettes, as Bridget Jones might say.

Woke up to find Great White Hope Number Two hoking round my drawer for the gold-star book. She reckons she deserves a full ten – and could well be right. Best not tell her I'm opening a whole new chart for Sue McEwan.

According to this morning's Guardian, Stormount mightn't be up and running until after the 2005 Westminster elections, which could mean two more years of this. So after breakfast, I rang Tommy Bowtie and told him that we've all had our fun, and it's time for me to get back to the real world.

Christ, I would have got more sympathy from Tony Soprano.

"'Fraid you've got to stay put," said Tommy. "King Size Barkley spent over ten grand on your campaign. And if King Size doesn't get a decent return, Fr Know-All will hear the full story about you, his niece, and the broken sacristy table. Or maybe the one about you, his other niece and why the school's camcorder is still missing.

"Bottom line is that you do this or you'll wind up teaching in prison. Though from what I hear, you mightn't like the way they practise their French in there."

"So what the hell am I supposed to do for two years?" I demanded.

"Open an office," said Tommy. "You can still draw the expenses from Stormount, and you could employ one of the Great White Hopes as your secretary."

He has a point about the office – at least it'll keep me out of mischief during daylight hours. But I'm damned if I'm hiring either of the GWHs. It'll only give them a chance to keep tabs on me. No way. I think I'll ring Sue McEwan for some advice.

Friday, December 5
Got a shop window on Dunavady Main Street, courtesy of King Size Barkley, so we'll hang a sign out tomorrow and open the office on Monday.

All things considered, it was very bad form of Tommy Bowtie to pass himself off as my constituency manager to the Stormount people. Bad enough that he got me 35 grand a year in administration expenses, but then, before I saw a dime, he signed up both the GWHs without telling me.

Number One is to be PA, and Number Two will be receptionist. Or is it the other way about? Not that it matters. I'd be as well painting a big bullseye on my back and sitting in the middle of Ballykelly rifle range.

I wonder could I report myself for shady hiring practices? Probably not. Two Fenian women, west of the Bann – Jesus, I could wind up with a medal from the Equality Commission. Besides, neither of the GWHs is related to me. And that's a lot more than you could say for a couple of the Antrim MLAs I met at the count-centre, whose PAs are not only their sisters but their wives as well.

Tommy Bowtie, who is married this long time and now has only an academic interest in women, is totally unapologetic and tells me it'll be good for me.

He has this theory he calls the Hierarchy of Politics, Relationships and Socks, which he will tell you about, any time he slips the leash.

Level One is the bachelor: You are a young capitalist who chooses whatever women and socks you like and then discards them when the colour starts to fade. If you need another woman or new socks, you just go out into the free market and procure them.

Level Two is the committed boyfriend: You are a democrat, who still believes firmly in the concept of choice. But you are more or less faithful to your woman, and while you feel free to buy your own socks, you tend not to bother.

Level Three is the fiancé: You are a post-Gorbachev communist, whose wife-to-be allows you a drawer full of socks, so you still have the illusion of choice.

Level Four is the married man: You are now part of a Stalinist regime where there is never more than one pair of socks in the drawer. And it doesn't matter that they're always grey, because so is your life.

Level Five is the beaten docket: You live in Albania and aren't allowed socks because you'd only run off to the pub.

Tommy Bowtie, needless to say, has been barefoot and wearing Moses sandals this long time. But he is also a sadist and believes it is time I graduated to Level Two. The two GWHs, meanwhile, are cock-a-hoop as they reckon it's now a straight race for the title.

Didn't drink at all last night; this is a time for massive self-control.

Saturday, December 6

The Secretary of State is inviting me to a Review of the Good Friday Agreement to start after Christmas, which, he promises, will run for a very limited time.

Bet my eyeteeth it doesn't start till February and will last about a week before the unionists find some way to throw an electric fire into the bath.

My own money's on September before anything moves. No-one is going to play kiss-catch with the other children, until the Euro elections in June. Apart maybe from the Alliance Party, who, let's face it, are the ugly girl at the back of the class and will kiss anybody. And we all know that as soon as you start snogging the Alliance, none of the good-looking girls is ever going to take you seriously. Likewise, there'll be no progress during the summer to allow all the madmen to go marching while the smart money heads straight the hell out of here.

The Irish News was reporting new speculation about a merger between the SDLP and Fianna Fáil, which had me a little flustered for a while. Officially, of course, I am non-party, but FF printed all my posters on the qt because of Uncle Shay.

The idea, however, of linking up with the Stoops, or indeed with the Shinners for that matter, is a non-starter. I've spent the past three years avoiding any public comment on the new police service, and I'm damned if I'm going to start now. You'd be safer taking a stance on the woman's right to choose.

Join the Stoops, and they'll stick you on a District Policing Partnership, so the dissidents can leave ticking boxes outside your door. Cuddle up to the Shinners, and they'll put out statements in your name condemning the reconstructed RUC, and the Orangies will come round and put in your new plate-glass windows.

Mr Rock, meet Mrs Hard Place.

So, I rang Fianna Fáil central office and asked for two minutes on the blower with Bertie, if he had it. Was told I could get five with some chap called Biffo, if I rang him immediately. He got straight to the point.

"Sorry, I don't know who you are or what you're talking about," he said. "Now, fuck off and never ring this number again."

Nothing to worry about on the merger front just yet, so.

Tuesday, December 9

I took Sue McEwan out to dinner after the office opening last night to thank her for coming up from Omagh to be my token Prod. And also, because she is the only woman I know who is still speaking to me.

Fr Know-All was an easy choice to perform the tape cutting, given that I have absolutely no political allies and he is pretty much acceptable to nationalists of all hues. Oh, and if I went past him, I'd never work as a teacher anywhere in the Six Counties again.

The downside to putting a member of the clergy in charge was rapidly apparent. As the late, great Senator Seamus Gallagher used to say: "If you want to get home early, never leave a priest in charge of a live mike."

So, as soon as Fr Know-All got the nod, the five-minute speech I'd asked for was always going to last an hour. Indeed, it's a good job I'd the wit to let him see me sneaking a bottle of gin out of a filing cabinet, or we'd have been there all night.

The real bother began afterwards at the wine and cheese buffet, when Fr Know-All told me how delighted he was that I'd hired his youngest sister's only daughter as my receptionist. GWH Number

Two, needless to say, has never mentioned this – the devious little witch has been playing the long game.

Nice move, babe, but you're in the big leagues now. So I called her aside and advised her that now I'm her employer, we must have a fully professional relationship – in case the Stormount mandarins get the wrong idea.

Surprisingly, Number Two took it quite well, on the surface at least. But five minutes later, while I'm glad-handing King Size Barkley, Number One comes over in a fit of tears and snotters and asks is it true I'm ditching her as well and that the whole gold-star scheme is shutting down for good.

After that, as the footballer said to the model, the only way to go was down. The upshot was that both the Great White Hopes quit their jobs, Fr Know-All got to see his niece tipping a pint of Guinness over my lap, and I'm a one-man-band in the office for the foreseeable future.

No bother to you, Tommy Bowtie.

And there was little sympathy either from Sue in the Delacroix restaurant back in Derry afterwards.

Over soup, I learned that I was a sexist pig, who regarded women as nothing but playthings. And yes, in retrospect, it was probably a bad idea to try and argue that girls are fully rounded intellectual beings but can still be playthings, if they want to be.

Over fillet steak, I learned that I was a republican pig, who regarded Protestants as nothing but interlopers and land thieves. And again, in retrospect, it wasn't my smartest hour to counter that with, "Yes, but what's your point?"

And over crème brûlée we had the full hallelujah chorus of: You're an Emotional Cripple, Afraid to Take Life Seriously. I didn't even bite on this one, as I was busy trying to look into Sue's flashing green eyes without being caught. And besides, I get to hear it every time I visit my mother.

After coffee – during which we established that my insecurity and fear of intimacy stemmed from me being an only child – I walked Sue to the carpark.

"I've had worse dates," I said to her. "'Course, I was sharing a prison cell with the World Gay Wrestling Champion at the time…"

"So you've experience of being a plaything yourself, then?" she grinned.

"Learned a few wrestling grips as well, if you ever want me to demonstrate…" I countered.

"I'm a karate black-belt," she said. "Put one hand on me and I'll break all your ribs."

"You'll forgive me if I pass up a goodnight kiss, so," I laughed.

"Damned right you will," she said. "I know too many places where that mouth of yours has been."

"Personally, I think you're scared of a challenge," I retorted. "Besides, let's face it, you could never go for anyone who wouldn't dance to your Orange tune."

"I am not a bigot," she snapped, very quickly. "And anyway, we've already agreed that you're the one who needs to develop."

"Okay then," I replied, giving her my most innocent smile, "so what you're saying is that you're afraid to give an emotional cripple a hand up?"

And with that, Dear Diary, she leaned over and kissed me on the cheek before skipping off laughing to her silver Beamer.

"Don't forget you're my token Fenian on Friday week," she shouted back. "But don't worry. I'll hide all the sharp objects in case you know my secretaries."

Thursday, December 11

Got the letter this morning to confirm that they're only going to pay us 70 percent of our Stormount salaries until the institutions are up and running.

Bastards. We'll have to slum it on £32,000, plus exies.

The DUP, fair play to them, have hit on a pretty novel way to raise the difference. They've collected all the SDLP's 'Stop the DUP' election posters, Big Ian is autographing them, and they're flogging them off at £40 a shot.

Personally, I wouldn't pay 40 pence for a Stoop poster – I mean, if you want to frighten off the neighbours' weans, there's always Alex

Maskey or David Trimble. But the Dups seem to have a market.

The DUP, interestingly, have also spent the past week tying themselves in knots about whether they've been talking to the Dublin government or not. Last Thursday, Doddsy dismissed the claims as "wild accusations" and somebody, somewhere, was threatening legal action. Though the clever bastards in Leinster House later confirmed there had been "social links".

Now today, it seems, the Dups are announcing they intend to take part in "full talks" with Bertie after Christmas – but they won't be discussing the "internal affairs of Northern Ireland".

Honest to God, your Honour, I'm a partial virgin.

Friday, December 12

If there is a more dangerous place in the world than a council meeting, it is the report of it two days later in the Derry Standard.

Wednesday night's business was very stormy – right down to the unionist walkout at the end. The row, naturally, was over the murder of Stumpy O'Rourke. And while Stumpy wasn't from this parish, his cousin Aileen is a Sinn Féin councillor here.

Aileen had learned the identities of the two gangsters who did the shooting and, boy, was she up on her high heels about it.

As you'd expect, it made the Standard's lead story:

UPROAR AS STUMPY'S 'KILLERS' NAMED
By Stan Stevenson

The entire unionist bloc stormed out of Wednesday night's meeting of Dunavady Council, after a motion to expel Aileen Bates, for identifying the alleged killers of Sinn Féin Assembly candidate John 'Stumpy' O'Rourke, was defeated.

Councillor Bates used chamber privilege to claim that Coleraine loyalists Rex Stovell and Wilbur Townslow had shot dead her cousin in Magherafelt six weeks ago. The Sinn Féin member said that the two men had already been "publicly congratulated" on the shooting on a loyalist website.

"The dogs on the street know they gunned down Stumpy," said Ms Bates. "They did it unmasked, in broad daylight, in front of half a dozen witnesses, who are now, unfortunately, too scared to talk.

"Just hours after the shooting, the LAG were gloating about it all over the internet. The administrator of the group's website even had the gall to thank 'Stovie' and 'Wilma' on a job well done. There's no doubt in my mind that this refers to Rex Stovell and Wilbur Townslow.

"Given that the PSNI either can't or won't stop these men, the least we can do is warn the public that they are living in our midst."

Ms Bates made her comments during Chairman's Business at the end of Wednesday's meeting, while councillors were debating a Sinn Féin motion to condemn Mr O'Rourke's murder.

But immediately after she spoke, the Sinn Féin council leader Chris Caddle stood up and announced that Ms Bates was speaking on her own behalf and had been strongly advised by her party leadership not to name names.

At this point, DUP alderman Tony Blunt proposed an emergency motion demanding Ms Bates's expulsion from the meeting and calling for her remarks to be struck from the record. The UUP and SDLP agreed to back the proposal. But Sinn Féin voted against, and the nationalist Shay Gallagher MLA abstained, so the motion fell by seven votes to six.

Disgust

After the vote was taken, UUP councillor Dexter Hart said he was disgusted with Shay Gallagher's "collaboration" in what was "essentially an IRA targeting exercise".

"If anything happens to these men, Mr Gallagher will have it forever on his conscience," said Mr Hart.

Mr Hart and the other three unionist councillors then walked out of the meeting.

What can I say? It was a complete abuse of privilege, and Aileen is round long enough to know better. Problem is, Stumpy was her cousin, and the whole county knows she's right about the two-man squad who killed him. Sure as shooting.

Saturday, December 13

Given previous experience, I thought I'd better beat a big dinner into me last night before heading up to the Derry Standard's Christmas bash. Not that I needed it though. It was so bad, I ended up staying for just a single drink. I'd have had more fun going on a stag night with the Women's Coalition.

The upstairs newsroom was packed with pols of all shades gossiping away. But as soon as I came through the door, it was as if someone had hit a mute button. The unionists, to a man, were firing daggers at me for sticking up for Aileen Bates. The Stoops were blaming me for leaking the Fianna Fáil merger reports. And the Shinners were still huffing because I'd asked one of their press officers for Mary Lou McDonald's private number.

The worst, however, was still to come. I knew that Sue McEwan was going to give me a hard time, but when she appeared in the foyer, she totally blanked me. As cold and sharp as sudden death.

She then ignored me for the ten minutes it took me to work the remnants of the little room. And indeed I thought she wasn't going to speak to me at all. But just as I'd finished my circuit and was about to head off to Da Vinci's, she came up behind me and gripped my wrist fiercely.

"Don't bother coming to Omagh next Friday," she hissed. "You'd only be taking car numbers anyway to pass on to your friends in the IRA."

"Don't be angry, Sue," I said quietly. "There are too many angry people in this room already."

But, by the time I had the words out, she'd already turned her beautiful head away, though not quick enough to stop me seeing how flushed her cheeks had got.

As I left, she was chatting to an extremely charming little man who you would never suspect was a Sinn Féin councillor. But I didn't even have the heart to wait to see her face when she found out.

Terrible thing anger. Uncle Seamus used to always say it was more infectious than any disease. "Far better to bury it than spread it about, son," was a favourite line.

On my way downstairs to the taxi, I ran into the guy who even I would concede is the most handsome man in Northern Ireland politics, Derry city councillor Gerry Diver. I'd give it all up in a heartbeat just to have his hair – it doesn't even look dyed.

So, after all that trauma, is it any wonder I woke up to find GWH Number One serving up tea and toast?

I know what you're thinking, Diary. But it's okay – she doesn't work for me any more.

Wednesday, December 17

The police called round to my one-man office this morning to tell me that my personal details had been published on the same loyalist website that had cheered on Stumpy's killers.

Apparently, if I had stood up for "true British principles", Aileen's remarks would have been rescinded and the Derry Standard would never have been allowed to identify the two mahoods.

I have to say, I was a bit queasy when I checked the web and saw they'd stuck up a big photograph of Dunavady Main Street, with my shop window marked off in a big white ring. Subtext: if you can't get him at home, go get him here.

The cops were barely out the door when the Standard rang, asking me to comment on this "outrageous attack on democracy".

Ninety percent of the time, reporters have the story written by the time they ring you, quotes and all, and are just running the lines by you to okay them. But I was a bit shaky today and wasn't for biting, so I referred Stan Stevenson to Tommy Bowtie and asked him not to publish the photo. I don't think he will, either – I'm the man who made sure he could publish the bad guys' names, and he owes me big time.

The only other thing interesting that happened today was some party officer from Fianna Fáil in Dublin rang and asked me if I would be interested in facilitating a private meeting between themselves and the SDLP Assembly group to discuss a possible "link-up".

Told him, and I quote directly: "Sorry, I don't know who you are or what you're talking about. Now, fuck off, and never ring this number again."

Thursday, December 18

I sent out the Christmas cards this morning, but no, I didn't write one to Sue McEwan. I haven't got the heart.

GWH Number Two is now completely off the scene, so Number One assumes that, as the only remaining contestant in the Big Brother household, she gets to have me for Christmas.

Two quick calls to the travel agency, however, gets it all sorted out. On Monday, I'm off to New York for a fortnight – on my own – to get over the shock of the death threat.

Number One is very understanding and assures me that we'll pick up again when I come back. Not if I see you first, kid. Sorry, but the number you are calling is no longer operational.

Friday, December 19

Tony Blunt from the DUP rang to say that, seeing as it's the season of goodwill, he'll call off the dogs if I apologise to the next council meeting for my "IRA-like" behaviour.

This is the same Tony Blunt who was caught with a jeepload of rifles for the Ulster Resistance 15 years ago – and beat the rap because the army claimed he was working for them undercover.

Told him to stick his offer where the telesales lady can put her colonic irrigation.

Saturday, December 20

Jeffrey now looks almost certain to jump ship to the DUP after David beat him round the Executive Room again. This will ensure that the UUP will be relegated off the top table, and no-one except Big Ian and the Shinners will have anything worth a damn to contribute to Tony Blair's "short, sharp" Review. So there'll be even less work in the New Year, if that's possible.

The good news today was that I got a call from Sue McEwan, thanking me for the flowers I sent to her office opening.

"Orange carnations," she said, "very appropriate."

"Bastards," I replied, "I ordered Easter lilies."

"I hear they're hoping to shoot you," she said, sounding a bit concerned.

"They can get in line," I replied, "...after the fleets of jealous husbands."

"Take care over the holidays," she laughed and clicked off.

And that, Dear Diary, was about as good a result as I got all week.

•••••••

The death threat was a new departure for Shay. He's normally very adept at staying out of trouble — correction, at not putting his neck on the line. But the 'naming' row blew up very quickly. If nothing else, it taught him the danger of thinking on your feet. Old Seamus would have been in the toilet when the vote was taken. When in doubt, shut your mouth, was a great saying of his.

The problem of working your way onto these death lists is that as your profile increases, so do your chances of making the next edition of *Lost Lives*. So there was backslapping all round when we managed to pack Shay off to the extended family in the States for the holidays. Fair play to King Size, it was his idea to get GWH Number One to invite him to Christmas dinner.

Sue McEwan was another complication we didn't need. Shay's been a sucker for red hair and green eyes all his life. I even got Dexter Hart's wife, Juliet, to ring Sue and warn her off. But Sue said she found him very charming — just like a little boy. Sue clearly doesn't have any little boys at home, or she'd know that they have ferocious appetites.

I accept the office opening wasn't my finest hour. But I warned Fr Know-All not to mention that he was related to Shay's new secretary. He'd have got a better reception if he'd announced she'd got herpes.

But it was my own fault for letting Shay into my theory of Women, Socks and Politics. Any time any woman looks like scratching the surface, he now has a cast-iron cop-out provided to him by his lawyer.

I suppose he may enjoy it while it lasts.

JANUARY 2004

By the time Shay returned from his holiday, he'd more or less resigned himself to a full-time political life.

The uncle's legend looms large in Dunavady, and Shay knows fine well that even if he gave up his council and MLA seats, people would expect him to keep doing the bloody work anyway. It's the family business.

The locals don't seem to mind the fact that he still lives in Derry city; that's where he was sired by his uncle's eldest brother Vincent. And I also think they prefer him to keep his carousing 20 miles down the road as it allows them to afford him a gravitas he'd certainly never get in Da Vinci's.

●●●●●●●

Tuesday, January 6

Flew back into Dublin early yesterday morning and just managed to make the Aer Arann connection into Derry, where I spent the rest of the day catching up on the papers.

The least said about New York the better. Suffice it to report that Cousin Teddy has never heard of anyone being barred from an entire Borough before, the doorman at 'Wet Girls Are Best' on Times Square has asked me to be Godfather to his baby son, and you probably shouldn't bless yourself from the Holy Water fonts outside St Patrick's Cathedral on Fifth Avenue.

Oh, and the only death threat I got was when I asked my table-dancer if she'd change of a ten.

Catching up on the papers back home, I see from the Irish News that we have finally unearthed the real reason Dublin left us high and dry in the early 1970s. Confidential documents released under the 30-year-rule reveal that Jack Lynch told Ted Heath he "couldn't afford" the North. Elsewhere, British ministers refer to the Irish cabinet as "timorous". For which I think we can read "cheap", "uninterested" and "gutless". But, of course, I knew that already, after four years at UCD.

Over on the sporting pages, I was delighted to see that the

Celtic manager Martin O'Neill has taken an OBE – we'll get a great rise out of all the Shinners on the council who travel across to the matches. He can call himself Queen Martina of Sheba, for all I care, as long as he keeps sticking it to Rangers.

Incidentally, I see from the Sunday Indo, that Gerry Adams was off in the States during the holidays as well – and raised $1.5 million for his party. Jesus, I came back flat broke.

I wonder would he be good for a sub?

Thursday, January 8

Re-opened the office to the general public this morning, and the man came and installed the internet.

First thing I did was to check myself out on the Assembly website. Oh all right, so, that's a lie – the first thing I actually did was to check out Sue Mack's entry, and boy, does that tell a story.

Full Name: *Agnes Susan McEwan*
DoB: *February 23, 1975* (Two years younger than I thought – go'n ya babe!)
Address: *Stranocum Road, Greencastle, Co. Tyrone*
Constituency Office Address: *As above*
Education: *BSc (Hons) in Food Science from UU Coleraine, 1996* (Standard culchie degree)
Occupation: *Senior Meat Inspector with the Department of Agriculture* (Write your own joke here…)
Hobbies: *Karate, Rally Driving, Leader with the Girls Brigade* (Could she BE more of a planter?)
But here, Dear Diary, is the money shot:
Family: *Unmarried. One daughter, Danielle, aged nine*

Sue, it seems, despite her complete indifference to the Gallagher charms, scored a few oats in her youth.

Happily, there is a Christmas card on my desk from her – so I'll be able to ring her and thank her for it later in the week. When I get my breath back and a plan together.

Spent the rest of the day counting my cards (typical insecurity of the only child). Got 101 in all, if you include the two 'In Loving Memory' cards with my name on them and the home-made 'Peace in Hell' card with the bullet inside.

Sent out exactly 200 – so I can happily take it that one in two people I know actually likes me, or at least is still speaking to me. Fifty percent approval – not bad for a politician.

Sunday, January 11

The papers are still full of Jeffrey's month-long adieu to David and his eventual 'realignment', last Thursday, with the Dups. Fair dues to him, he milked it better than the Old City Dairy.

I'm a little surprised Jeff's content to give up such a prominent position in the UUP to join the DUP's middle rankers. But all political ambition is a mystery to me anyway.

For my part, I intend to get out of the game and back to teaching the minute King Size Barkley drops the loaded revolver. Though I suppose as long as I'm stuck with it, I should get down to the Delacroix for a bit of schmoozing over a lunchtime pint.

I'd better wait, though, until Number One finishes up in the shower.

Wednesday, January 14

According to today's Guardian, Tony Blair has won a new award – for uttering the most embarrassing political cliché of all time.

Naturally enough, it's his line from Stormount on Good Friday 1998, when he told the world: "This is not a day for soundbites…but I feel the hand of history on our shoulders."

Six years on, and the only place history has its hand now is on Tony's short and curlies.

Thursday, January 15

The Review, we've been told, will open in a fortnight's time, with the initial sessions chaired by the two premiers. So, at last I had a half-decent pretext for ringing Sue Mack. I needed to suss out if there was any point in either of us going, given that we effectively cancel one another out.

I missed her at the office, so I rang her at home. A young girl answered, who told me Mommy wasn't about. So I decided to go fishing.

"What about your daddy?" I asked. "Is he around?"

"Nope," replied the girl, "the no-good bastard ran off before I was born."

"Aha," I said, "so who's looking after you?"

"What are you – a cop?" came the answer.

"No, my name's Shay," I laughed. "I'm a friend of your mother's – and you must be Danielle."

"I know all about you, Mr Gallagher," said Danielle. "I think 'friend' is a little strong, don't you?"

"So what exactly has your mother been saying about me?"

"Mostly that you're a sexist, Fenian shitehawk... What's a shitehawk?"

"It's like a sparrowhawk, only less polite," I told her.

"I think she secretly likes you, though," continued Danielle.

"And why's that?"

"Because she's kept one of the flowers you sent her, in a book. You know the ones you gave her to say sorry for joining the Provos."

"I didn't join the Provos, I just didn't vote against them," I insisted.

"First they came for the Jews, Mr Gallagher..."

"I have to run, Danielle. Will you tell your Ma I called?"

"What's it worth, so?"

"I'll take you to Disney On Ice at the Waterfront at the end of the month – if Sue lets me."

"Trying to sneak in the back door, Mr Gallagher? My mother's right – you couldn't be up to you."

Sue, fair play to her, rang back within half an hour. And to cut to the chase, we agreed to hold fire on going to the Review until we see if anyone is likely to be remotely interested in our contribution. And she gave me a qualified yes on the Disney gig.

"Do I have to come too?" she asked with a sigh.

"Sure you were in the UUP," I replied. "You're well used to

Mickey Mouse shows. Then again, you mightn't want to be seen in public with a Fenian shitehawk…"

"The little minx," laughed Sue. "What else did Danielle say?"

"Not a damn thing," I lied.

Friday, January 16

Christmas is over, and there's too little action for the media, so they're busying themselves making mischief. I had to get corrections from two of the papers yesterday for lumping my vote in with the Shinner camp, when they were doing their look-aheads to next week's Review. The Shinners are getting it in the teeth this weather from the DUP, UUP and McDowell in the South about their IRA and criminal links. It's very obviously a concerted thing, and I'd rather not get whacked in the crossfire.

Both the Shinners and the Stoops have made approaches to me over the past couple of weeks, talking about informal partnerships and what have you. But Tommy Bowtie advises me that as long as I'm here, there's a lot more mileage to be gained in remaining a Johnny-Kiss-All-The-Girls. Which, let's be frank, is my life's mission.

The rumour-mill's got so wild that there's even speculation that Billy Leonard is about to leave the SDLP for Sinn Féin. An ex-cop from the Shankill Road? Jesus, there's more chance of them letting an Englishman into the 'Ra.

Sunday, January 18

Last night's 'Top Ten' challenge in the bar was the Top Ten Reasons for Re-establishing Stormount.

We actually got about 30, but the majority aren't recordable for reasons of taste and decency:

- The Belfast mandarins in the NIO won't spend a red cent west of the Bann until suspension's lifted.

- The BBC have run out of valid adjectives to put in front of 'crisis'.

- George Bush might confuse IRA with IRAQ and start carpet-bombing us.

- Tony Blair might confuse IRA with IRAQ and start carpet-bombing us.

- Bertie Ahern might confuse IRA with IRAQ and allow the Brits to carpet-bomb us from Shannon Airport.

- The Sunday Independent have run out of ways to bitch about the governments caving in to the Shinners.

- We're not seeing enough of the DUP on the TV.

- Gallagher's weekly unit count is now in treble figures.

- Gallagher feels guilty cashing his paycheque when there are people working their arses off, doing real backbreaking labour, for about a quarter of what he's on.

- If Gallagher doesn't find something to keep him busy, GWHs Number One and Two are going to hang him, flay him and eat him alive. And not in a good way either.

Wednesday, January 21

Things at the office are starting to settle into a comfortable pattern since I got the new receptionist – a bright, young chap called Francis McNicholl, who's apparently known in GAA circles as Frank the Tank.

Francis got top marks at the interview when he gave a perfect answer to King Size's question: "How do you feel about the threats against Mr Gallagher's life?"

"They'll have to get through me first," said Francis, romping home at a canter.

Francis is already a big hit with the punters – probably because he's one of the most charming and easy-going people you'd ever meet. He's also proved a dab hand at keeping the outer sanctum running with minimum fuss – no mean feat given some of the people I get in here.

My clients tend to fit into five main categories. First, and most importantly, you have the headcases. These are people whose lives have been wronged by the system – and you, personally, are to blame. As a rule, they are very angry customers, with a range of assault-related convictions, and it is your responsibility to get them out of their latest jam. A perfect example of their number is James 'Bite Me' O'Boyle, who sits in the anteroom and barks like a dog until I agree to see him. Since Francis arrived, I now have a list at reception of about 20 of these individuals who must not be admitted, or allowed speak to me on the phone, under any circumstances. The only exception is when Bite Me is at the copshop and needs bail money. The last time I let him stew there, as soon as he got out he pulled the two wing mirrors off my car.

Next you have the guys (and dolls) who are basically dropping in for a chat and to let you know that you work for them. They will tell you, at great length, what is wrong with this world, what you should be doing, and how your uncle would have made a much better fist of things. Among this number, you would have the likes of Fr Know-All and Mrs Flynn, the Irish Dancing teacher and world-renowned political oracle.

Dealing with this type is a lot more difficult, so I took advice from a local doctor, who can't afford to give any more than seven minutes to any one patient. After that, he stands up and slowly helps them on with their coat. This trick works okay some of the time, but Fr Know-All just glares at you, like he knows he's getting the bum's rush. So in his case, I slap my forehead and announce that Bite Me O'Boyle, or one of the other crazies, has an appointment for two-minutes time – and Fr K, who gets enough of that at confession, is gone like a shot.

Thirdly, you have the people who take it for granted you're as crooked as they are and want to cut you in on a shady business proposition. There's the man in the bad suit who will give you ten percent of his company on the hush-hush, if you get him a grant he's not entitled to. And there's the pretty Czech lady who will give you 100 percent of something else entirely, if you just sign a piece of paper saying she's been living in the town for the past five years.

I send all these cases to Tommy Bowtie – and of course, they never go near him. Or so he says.

Occasionally, you get clients who will try to draw you into neighbourhood disputes. These tend to centre on issues such as land boundaries, re-dipped sheep, and, more often than not, playground fights. The best policy here is: listen to all sides and say nothing. And if you have to speak at all, refer them to someone else. Otherwise, you can only lose votes.

Finally, you have the genuine punters, in with genuine concerns. These can range from keeping court cases out of the newspapers, to making representations at council, to raising an issue with a Direct Rule minister. But most of the time, they're in to ask you how to prepare properly for a tribunal, where some government body or other is trying to screw them out of some meagre benefit.

Needless to say, the last group are my favourite by a mile. And if I'm to be honest, I have to say I prefer women clients to men, and not just the good-looking ones. Women are infinitely more reasonable than men – they're solution-focused and don't spend as much time fighting, whinging and blaming. But they do tend to call in too much; men tend not to visit until they've taken out a contract on their next-door neighbour and are wondering if maybe they've gone a little too far.

Monday, January 26

The SDLP have invited me to a 'Ding Dong the Witch is Gone' party on Saturday night to celebrate Big Ian's retirement from Europe. Personally, I think the celebrations could be a bit premature – I mean, if the Doc's not going to be in Strasbourg three days a week, it'll allow him a lot more time on his hands back here.

The Irish News is suggesting Ian Junior could be the successor. Can't see it myself. Junior may have his father's volume and he certainly has that same glassy-eyed stare, but little Pete the unterfuhrer is never going to let him drive off the back tees.

Couple of lady friends tell me that Junior's actually not a bad looking chap. Though I suppose if you've seen seven pages of Sammy Wilson in the buff, courtesy of the Sunday World, it's all relative.

Nice of the Stoops to invite me to their bash though – obviously they're still keeping their options open on the Fianna Fáil merger.

Tuesday, January 27

Spent the weekend talking a little treason with the Shinners. They've come up with a suggestion to curtail boy-racers in Dunavady, which may be a goer. They want to introduce a night-time curfew on all drivers under 25. But in return, they've found an insurance agent, who'll cut premiums in half, if the youngsters agree not to go out between 10.00pm and 6.00am.

At the moment, the bandits are gathering at every garage forecourt, lay-by and school playground from Drumbridge to Garvagh. And the Glenshane Pass after dark has more sudden bangs than an Al Qaeda training camp.

The SF proposal seems sensible enough to me. Only problem is, they need my vote to get it through council. And if I'm seen backing them again, it'll only remind the boys in the red, white and blue balaclavas that they still haven't dealt with me.

So I put it to the Shinner council leader Chris Caddle that maybe I should propose the motion – and they weigh in behind me instead. And surprisingly, he agreed – as long, of course, as he gets doing all the TV and radio. Which he's very welcome to.

We decided that I should sound out the Dups on the plan as well – given that we didn't want it to look like a complete set-up, and also because Tony Blunt is an insurance agent himself and might actually have something useful to contribute for a change.

So before talking to Blunt, I called Sue Mack to pick her brain on how best to approach him.

"Offer him a chance to amend the proposal slightly," she advised me. "If they think that they're part of it and have contributed to it, they'll probably roll with it.

"But you knew that anyway. You just want to know if I've remembered about Friday night and our big Disney date. And yes, despite all my attempts to contract a terminal illness and talk sense into my daughter, it's still on. We'll meet you in the Europa Bar at seven. We'll be the ones with the bags over our heads."

Thursday, January 29

The boy racers' motion went through like a song last night after I incorporated the DUP's suggestion that the council would compile a panel of insurance companies to service young people who agreed to the curfew and not just recommend a single broker.

Of course, it was the Shinners that did all the incorporating – though Tony Blunt will never know that. Better again, I'm now back in Mr Blunt's good books, which significantly lowers my chances of waking up with a shroud round me. For the moment, at least.

But the best news of all is that I'm going to Disney On Ice tomorrow night – with young Danielle McEwan and her babe of a mother. It doesn't even matter that it's in Belfast.

I haven't been this excited since I was 15 and Deirdre O'Connell got her braces off. Might have to give GWH Number One a call – see if she can calm me down any.

Saturday, January 31

Not often I visit you on a Saturday, Diary. But there are some things that just can't wait.

Got to the Europa at seven on the dot – there's no room for the play-it-cool, seven-minute rule, with these Orange women. You give a time, you're there – otherwise you're toast.

But when I went into the bar, there was no sign of Sue or Danielle, so I ordered up a double vodka and tonic and found a corner.

By 7.30 there was still no sign, so I waved over for another double and was just about to take a healthy chug, when I spotted Sue come in at the far door, on her own and looking a little flustered.

"Where's the nipper?" I asked, as she flopped down in an armchair opposite me.

"In bed with tonsillitis," said Sue, lifting my glass and tipping it to her head. "She took bad when she came in from school at four o'clock. I've been trying to get you ever since, but your phones were off. I would have rung and left a message here in the bar except I knew you'd take the hump. So I drove up to tell you myself."

Up close, she looked stunning. She was wearing this blue silk dress, split just high enough and cut just low enough to send my head dizzy. Every pair of eyes in the room was on her.

It was all I could do to steady my voice and ask her could she use another drink.

"Could Bill Clinton use a new dry-cleaner?" she grinned.

I flagged down a passing waitress who immediately brought us two more of the same.

"Better drink up quickly," I said, "if we're going to get to this show."

And then, Dear Diary, it happened.

"Just one damn minute," snapped Sue. "I work a 90-hour week in a ten-by-eight room that is one step up from a prison cell. I spend my days advising farmers, whose trousers are held up with string, how to access EU grants. I then get to spend every other waking moment with a snotty nine-year-old kid – who incidentally has never been sick a day in her life before now.

"I am a 28-year-old girl who still lives at home with her God-fearing mother – a woman whose idea of fun is playing 'Bait The Fenian' at Drumcree barricade. And, most importantly of all, I'm after spending £250 on this Prada dress, which you – you stupid big Provo – still haven't mentioned.

"So after all that, if you think I'm going to spend my first night away from home – IN SIX YEARS – watching Donald Fucking Duck, you're very much mistaken. There's only one place I'm going. I'm in room number 207. You've got five minutes."

I made it in two.

●●●●●●●

Christ, he doesn't leave a terrible lot to the imagination.

We were all certain Shay had blown his chances with Sue before Christmas, but he bounces back quicker than Peter Mandelson — and is twice as deadly. His great strength is that he refuses to dwell on the negative.

It's like the death threat. Shay was convinced that because

he'd heard nothing for a couple of weeks, it was all over and done with. People who live on west bank Derry have had it quiet too long — they forget how vulnerable the rest of the North is. That's why we got him Frank the Tank. Though even then we had to overrule Shay's determined attempts to appoint Miss Drumbridge with the six-inch heels.

Frank overcame any initial resistance on the very first day, however, when, without prompting, he blew off both the GWHs in the space of about five minutes — telling them that Shay was in meetings all day and couldn't be disturbed by anyone. Frank, God be good to him, had the ideal pedigree. His family were from the town, and he'd graduated with a first in politics. And it wasn't long before he and Shay were as tight as skin on a stick.

I'd also wired off Frank, privately, to keep an eye on Shay's visitors' list. There are a lot of sharks floating about these waters, and we couldn't have Shay selling off the fishing rights for a bagful of magic beans. He's generally cute enough to chase all the carpetbaggers up to me. But you've got to be careful. If anyone's going to get rich on Shay's watch, it's going to be me.

FEBRUARY 2004

I think it's my role in life to be the guy who gives Shay Gallagher his wake-up calls. It's not something I particularly enjoy, but in this case, there was no way I was going to watch him messing Sue about like the rest of his feather-headed fan club.

Shay was already well aware that Sue had a child while she was at college — actually, he was making a virtue of the fact that he was liberal enough to date a single mother. But he was only paddling in the shallow end; Sue needed someone who wasn't afraid of the deep water.

She'd learnt to swim the hard way. The only daughter of a high court judge, Sue got drunk for the first time ever at her Freshers' Ball and woke up pregnant. Just to complete her triumph, the donor was the neighbourhood lowlife, who'd only snuck into the disco to bag himself a young one — and was gone quicker than her hangover.

I have to say that when the news broke around the courts, there were a few ripe remarks about how the new baby wasn't the first McEwan to have only one notarised parent. But Sue had stuck her chin out, sucked up the abuse and spent the next decade working hard, getting her degree and rearing her daughter.

Yes, Sue's career as a wild child ended after only six hours of university, and she's been paying for it ever since. When her father popped his clogs five years ago, he'd barely hit the carpet before Old Ma started blaming Sue for sending him to an early grave. No mention, of course, of the 40 Dunhill-a-day he'd smoked since he was 18 and the nightly bottle of Scotch to drown out his wife.

A few years ago, an old university buddy of mine, now practising in Omagh, tried to entice Sue out to dinner. But he was shot down quicker than an LVF drug dealer. And it was generally accepted she'd given up the game for good. Then, along came that deadly Gallagher charm, and before you could say Run Like Fuck, he'd started working on how to break her heart again.

Not that it was any of my business, but Sue deserved better. And besides, Shay had to learn that there are other ways of taking advantage of someone than waiting until the fifth drink kicks in. So I asked Shay, for once in his life, to walk away.

●●●●●●●

Monday, February 2

That Tommy Bowtie has a neck like a jockey's bollix.

I ran into him at the end of the Bloody Sunday rally at Free Derry Corner, and he said he needed to talk to me about something. Urgently. So we headed over to the City Hotel for some serious conversation.

I thought it might have been a new loyalist threat, but he just shook his head and said listen up. No, what he wants is for me to dump Sue. Apparently, I'm too much of a flake for her and am wasting her time.

Jesus, he was deadly serious. He's had a knot in his gut ever since Mrs Bowtie cut him off when Tommy Jr. was born eight months ago. And now he wants me to come sit in the corner with the rest of the Frustrated Old Drunks.

I asked him how much he was billing me for this advice – seeing as he normally charges £200 an hour to tear apart marriages. But he just glared and told me that if I didn't grow up I'd be paying him £200 to remove his fist from my mouth.

After that, it just got silly. Tommy threatened to give out my new mobile number to the two GWHs – and if I didn't move quickly, he'd give them Sue's numbers as well. I reminded him that two could play at that and offered to pass on all his private numbers to Fr Know-All and Bite Me O'Boyle. Tommy ended up stomping out of the hotel with three-quarters of a drink still in front of him.

The most worrying thing about all this, however, is that he might have a point – and if it were anybody but Sue, I might be listening to him. But, as the pair of us were shouting the odds over our hot whiskeys, I realised something important: for the first time in my life, I don't want to cut and run.

Wednesday, February 4

The Review proper begins today, so it was down to the Omagh Leisure Centre last night for a televised RTE debate on the 'big issues' chaired by Miriam O'Callaghan.

I was relegated to the kiddies' table, but wasn't too worried as

I got to sit beside Sue Mack, who was looking deadly in this Louis Vuitton miniskirt suit. (Hope the camera didn't pick up the shake in my hand.)

The whole programme went pretty much as expected – plenty of finger pointing, a few naughty digs, and lots of wolf-whistles when Gerry Kelly took off his jumper, because "it's too hot in here". Aye, right.

Kelly, so I'm told, has long been the Shinners' in-house babe-magnet. And he achieved full Johnny Depp status a couple of years back when he broke out of a pair of police handcuffs during the Ardoyne standoff. Can't see the attraction myself – though I'll grant you he's got more balls than Adidas.

The opening segment of the show saw Gerry and the UUP's Reg Empey go head-to-head over policing. Gerry was holding out for Patten, Reg was holding out for Semtex, while the rest of us were holding out for the commercial break. Christ, if there's anyone left on this island who doesn't know these arguments by heart, he should consider himself the luckiest bastard alive.

Mark Durkan then got sucked into the brawl when the UUP contingent in the audience started teasing him about the SDLP's losses in November. Durks, however, did well to point out that the Ulster Unionists were the only party who'd actually lost three MLAs SINCE the election, so that settled them down for a while.

After the interval, a few DUP diehards in the gallery asked Durkan to comment on the Sunday Life reports that some of the Belfast Stoops were preparing to launch a coup against him. The Derryman, however, wasn't a damned bit fazed and said his party would survive whoever was at the helm. The DUP, he pointed out, couldn't survive a week without Paisley – "it would be like the Muppets without Kermit".

Part three of the show saw Michael McDowell, the Republic's Minister for Punishment and Retribution, light into both Durkan and Gerry Kelly for their watery stance on the Provos. I often thank Jesus that McDowell wasn't born in the North. He's the scariest man I've ever met who's not in the IRA.

Mitchel McLaughlin, who was in the audience off to the side, then launched right back into McDowell, sparking quite a lively ding-dong. Mitchel's TV image has improved dramatically since he shed the Village People moustache, but he's always been a solid defender for the Shinners when the IRA feck up in style. This point, of course, wasn't missed on McDowell, who said Mitchel reminded him of the wee boy telling the rent collector, "Swear to God, mister, my mammy says there's no-one in." But Mitchel got the biggest laugh of the night when he retorted that McDowell was the man Mammy sends out to frighten the rent-collector away.

Back at the top table, Gregory Campbell didn't miss the opportunity to get the boot into the UUP over the recent defections. Gregory is a seasoned political street fighter and has brought many of the qualities that saw him become a top junior footballer to the trade. Gregory, it's said, would always hit you a kick in the tunnel on the way out to the pitch, for fear he wouldn't see you during the game.

He came in for a bit of teasing himself over the Dups' first ever meeting with the Taoiseach last weekend. David Ervine of the PUP asked him why they didn't throw snowballs at Bertie Ahern and shout: "No Pope here", like they did when Lemass came to the North in the 1960s. Durks then shouted up: "Because it was raining." And Campbell went as red as a Sacred Heart lamp.

Gregory then retorted that Ervine was performing quite well for a man who didn't speak English as his first language. So Miriam wisely went to a break before anybody's handbag got damaged.

In the last section of the show, I managed to get my neb in when I was asked about the prospects of a Fianna Fáil merger with the SDLP. I scored a nice round of applause, I have to say, when I passed it over to Mark Durkan, telling Miriam, "I'm sure he would be much better at not answering this question than I would."

After the programme, Sue Mack and myself headed for a drink in the Mellon Country Inn. Unfortunately for us though, the entire Shinner contingent arrived in for a debriefing, and there were a few digs flying over that Gallagher seems to be involved in lots of secret mergers these days.

So we sneaked off and cancelled the room.

Thursday, February 5

Few interesting postscripts to last week's trip to Belfast.

First, I got Francis to check all my phones and discovered that no-one – no-one at all, that is – had attempted to contact me at home, at the office or on the mobile between three o'clock and seven o'clock on Friday evening. Sue's mobile must have been faulty; either that or she's not half as cool as she's letting on, perish the thought.

Secondly, the Prada dress Sue was wearing at the Europa actually cost £450 and not £250, while her camisole cost another £85. I checked their catalogue on the web.

And thirdly, Danielle made a miraculous recovery and we're going to take back her to the ice show tomorrow night.

Wonder if I slip her another score, could she break a limb?

Sunday, February 8

I'm really going to like Danielle. On Friday, at the Disney show, she spent the entire time mortifying her mother to such an extent that, by the end of the night, Sue was going to let her drive her Beamer just to get her to stop.

It started as soon as I got into the car in the Europa carpark on the way to the Waterfront.

"Mr Gallagher," said Danielle innocently, "are you going to be my new daddy?"

Sue's face lit up like a brake lamp and the Opal Fruit I was sucking on shot out of my mouth in surprise and hit the windscreen. But then there was this little giggle from the back seat, and a voice went: "Gotcha!" And I knew we were in for a good night.

When we got to our seats, Danielle – who is her mother's Mini-Me, though without the hang-ups – winked over and whispered me to watch. She then loudly insisted on swapping places, because Mommy told her on the journey up that she wants to hold hands with her new boyfriend.

At the interval, when I bought the drinks, Danielle thanked me and told me I was so much nicer than that mean old dentist who took them out last month and wouldn't buy her sweets. And I was much cleaner than that greasy accountant guy before

Christmas, who picked his nose all the time. And I was a lot better looking than any of the culchie Omagh politicians that Mommy usually goes out with.

"Stop it," laughed Sue, with a slight hysterical edge to her voice. "I haven't been on a date since Eddie Irvine got his first go-cart. And is it any wonder? You'd better start behaving yourself, Danielle, or I'll tell your granny you were nice to a Fenian."

"That's another thing," continued Danielle, "I'm to refer to you as Mervyn in the house."

"Not true! Not true!" protested Sue, before casting her eyes to heaven and conceding, "okay, okay...that part's true."

And so it went on, with the daughter starting fires with gay abandon and the mother struggling hopelessly to put them out. I haven't laughed so hard since Fr Know-All fell into the bishop's grave.

The pièce de résistance, however, was when they left me back to my car on Glengall Street.

"Mommy," said Danielle. "You know the way I was supposed to come here with you last week...?"

"Yes," replied Sue.

"And you know the way Nana looked after me, while you went up to Belfast to explain to Mr Gallagher...?"

"Y-es," said Sue, very hesitantly.

"Well, when are you going to pay me the tenner you promised me for letting on to be sick?"

Sue just put her head in her hands and groaned, "Oh God, take me now."

"Not to worry, Sue," I grinned back in at her. "She caught me for 20."

Back in the Land That Time Forgot, today's papers are full of the DUP's 'magna carta' for breaking the political deadlock. This basically boils down to: throw out the Shinners; get the tame Catholics to come to heel; and reinstate majority rule.

Did I miss something, or didn't we just have 30 years of war to put an end to exactly that?

Wednesday, February 11

Fun and games at last night's council meeting – I did well not to walk into another tempête de merde.

It all started when the SDLP put forward a motion noting "with sadness" John Hume's decision to retire from both Westminster and Europe and congratulating him on his outstanding achievements as a politician – and in particular, bringing the IRA in from the wilderness.

The Shinners, obviously, wanted to delete this dig at them – and to include instead the proviso that "the SDLP will never again have such a brilliant leader". Which also was quite naughty.

The Shinners needed my vote to get their amendment through, and after my pre-Christmas experience, this wasn't going to happen. But if I sided with the SDLP, the unionist bloc would undoubtedly weigh in to vote down the Provos, and community activists would be putting in my windows.

So, given the choice between a grave and a cold hole in the ground, I did what all fair-minded cowards do and went to the toilet. As Uncle Seamus, God rest him, used to say, there is absolutely no money in playing 'Who's-the-Better-Looking-Sister?'.

The Dups, however, then tabled a motion of their own congratulating Big Ian for resisting solidly all Hume's attempts to bring about Dublin involvement in Ulster. But this fell when Tony Blunt couldn't get a seconder.

I think we ended up with a composite motion wishing John well on his retirement and applauding him for opening the Dunavady Credit Union.

The UUP's Dexter Hart, the mischievous dog, then proposed a motion congratulating "one particular" member of the council for his own efforts to promote "Protestant-Catholic" harmony. "I understand," said Dexter to loud guffaws, "that this man, who insists on remaining anonymous, regularly runs cross-community trips to Disney On Ice – and sometimes even throws in bed and breakfast."

If the Derry Standard print a word, I'll clean them out.

Monday, February 16

Sue Mack was in London at the Labour Women's Conference, so it was a long old weekend at home. I've ruled the GWHs off limits, even for emergencies, so I took Danielle to the pictures to find out how I'm getting on.

Old Ma McEwan wasn't wild about me calling at the house, but like the rest of the world, she now knows fine well what's happening and at least prefers things out front where she can see them. I sucked up to her by telling her that it wasn't hard to see where her daughter and granddaughter got their good looks – you'd be surprised how often corn like that works. Old Ma, however, was impervious. "A Fianna Fáiler," she moaned. "You don't even have the bottle to be a proper Provo. Thank God Sue's father isn't alive, or he'd have died of shame."

On the way to the Omagh Multiplex, Danielle told me I was pushing all the right buttons with her mother, apart from my two obvious handicaps: one, I'm a Fenian; and two, Mommy says I wreck more hearts than the Ulster Fry.

She also let another little secret slip as we tried to get into Looney Tunes 2. The film was packed out, so I volunteered to take her to Scooby Doo 2, showing on the next screen.

"I've already seen it on DVD," said Danielle.

"But that's not possible," said the receptionist. "It's not out yet."

"Nope," countered Danielle, "I've seen it already – and Shrek 2 as well."

Mommy, it seems, occasionally lives on the edge – and buys pirate movies at Omagh market…

We went to Scooby regardless, where Danielle drank an entire litre of Coke. But she begged me not to tell her gran, as apparently Coke sends her hyper. Needless to say, I stopped at the supermarket afterwards to let Danielle beat another big bottle into her before she went home.

Thursday, February 19

The police arrested the two loyalists who shot Stumpy – Rex Stovell and Wilbur Townslow – first thing on Tuesday morning. It looks like it was just a show, however, as they were out again by teatime – and I got a bullet in a sympathy card this morning. I'm going to have to talk to the cops about getting reinforced windows and maybe a CCTV camera for the office. The Northern Ireland Office will pick up the tab, so it's pointless not to.

I needed cheering up, so I visited Tommy Bowtie and got him to ring Sue and pretend he was from the Film Piracy Branch of the PSNI. He told her they'd caught a dealer in Omagh market, and his defence was, "Sure I'm selling them to that big rip of a politician with the red hair and long legs."

Sue, fair play to her, protested that she didn't know what he was talking about. So Tommy said he'd rung the house last night and got talking to a child. And in the throes of the chat, the child had confirmed watching Shrek 2 and Scooby Doo 2 on DVD in her home.

Sue still played dumb, so Tommy said he had a search warrant for both her home and her computer, which he would be executing in the next six hours.

"Actually," he said, "we don't normally give any notice at all, but seeing as you're an MLA, we're being careful to give you due warning. If you know what I mean."

Well, this really put the wind up Sue, as not only was her house going to be raided but the cops were actually proposing to collude with her to make sure nothing was found.

"I need to talk to my lawyer," she replied in a weak voice, stunned at how quickly and easily her political career had come to an end.

Tommy couldn't keep it up.

"Don't worry," he said. "We'll be very discreet. We'll not even bring handcuffs. Anyway, Shay Gallagher says you've your own pair…"

Tommy then held the phone away from his ear as the redheaded bomb exploded. I never knew a lady who could swear so passionately.

So, I let her blow off the worst of it and then took the phone to begin a very long apology.

"I'm sorry, I'm sorry, I'm sorry," I told her. "It was just a joke. Forgive me."

"No way," she snapped, though the ice was starting to melt. "You're a low-down Provo dog."

"And you're a beautiful Orange witch," I countered.

"You're not going to charm your way out of this, Gallagher."

"No, really, I'm sorry. Really sorry. Forgive me, please… I love you."

I love you?? Now, where the hell did that come from? Rewind that damn tape. I want a recount.

Saturday, February 21

Lots of TV footage of last night's arrests in city-centre Belfast. The cops claim the IRA were attempting to kidnap a dissident republican from a bar when they were intercepted.

Tommy Bowtie, who was over at my flat escaping from the youngsters for an hour, said the coverage was better than NYPD Blue. But he didn't think that's what Gerry Adams had in mind when he asked for a takeaway from Kelly's Cellars.

Wednesday, February 25

The unionist bloc tried to suspend last night's Policy and Resources meeting of the council to discuss the weekend incident in Belfast and its political implications. Both the DUP and the UUP thought it would be a good idea to try the arrested men in Dunavady Town Hall and string them up afterwards on the flagpole outside.

The Shinners pointed out, however, that if everything else in the weekend papers were true, Elvis is now living on a moon colony, and George Best will never take another drink.

The town solicitor then advised that the Kelly's Cellars incident was undoubtedly sub judice and that everyone should stop talking about it. He also emphasised that no-one was being charged with IRA membership. And thankfully, the Stoops closed ranks with SF to rule out any more discussion – so making my vote academic.

•••••••

The repeated threats from Stovell's gang were worrying me a lot more than they were Shay. He was far too cavalier. The CCTV and bombproof windows should have been installed the day he moved into the office. Typical Derryman, he thought it was all a game. Maybe if he'd been living out here, where they can come for you in the night, he might have been a little more circumspect. Was he expecting these guys to send him their fixture list?

Eventually, I took matters into my own hands and spoke to the director of security in Stormount. When she heard the nature of the threats against Shay, she immediately offered me 15 grand to fix up the office. I also got a guarantee that the cameras and armoured glass would be installed by their own in-house crew by the end of the month.

Don Juan's mind, however, was still on other things. Big slushy bastard. Nothing a few nights walking the floor with a puking child wouldn't cure.

MARCH 2004

The problem with players like Shay is that sooner or later they meet people who take the game a lot more seriously than they do.

We always knew that some day he was going to crash into a woman who would tell him where to stick his little-lost-boy act. Just as we always knew that his smartass contempt for small-town politics was going to land him in a whole pile of bother. We just didn't figure it was all going to happen in the one week.

It gave me no satisfaction at all to say: "I told you so." Well, all right then — it did a little. If only because he'll think twice before calling me a frustrated old drunk again.

•••••••

Monday, March 1

Spent the weekend at the First Annual Ulster Scots Shindig in Newtownstewart to make up with Sue. Dear Lord. I haven't seen so many blowhards, munchkins and fans of bad music gathered in the one place since Willie McCrea made his last video.

It opened on Friday night with a ceili-cum-linedancing spectacular. An Ulster Scots ceili, it seems, is exactly like an Irish one, except all the good bits are taken out. For a start, the musicians were all Scottish and couldn't play in tune; secondly, no-one knew any of the dances, because they were all invented just last week by some chancer from Larne on a big Stormount grant; and thirdly the uileann pipes were replaced with bagpipes, which for us purists, is like removing a grand piano from a chamber orchestra and installing a very loud farting machine.

Needless to say, as the closest thing they had to a celebrity couple, Sue and I were dragged out to shake our stuff. And the best thing I can say about that is that I'm 100 percent certain that no-one I know — or at least care about remotely — saw us. Indeed, if there was another papist in the place, he spent the night hiding in the toilets.

On a happier note, however, Sue had some serious making up of her own to do that night…

Next morning, we had workshops, which offered a choice between a History of the Ulster Scots in America and a course in How Till Speke Your Hamely Tung.

Couldn't subject myself to the guy with the bad Ballymena accent, and as a teacher I object in principle to any language that translates 'pupils with special needs' as 'wee daft yins'. So instead I got three hours of how President Andrew Jackson may have been born in East Antrim and how the guy who wrote Red Sails in the Sunset was from Portstewart. Be still ma hart.

After a tour of the Folk Park in the afternoon, we had a dinner of haggis, scotch eggs and bread'n'butter puddin', which was made a little more bearable by the fact the event was sponsored by Bushmills. So by the time we got up from the table, we were speeking Ullans like two wee nitifs.

The worst, however, was yet to come. After dinner, the organisers had laid on a four-hour Riverdance-style spectacular, based on the life of Ulster's greatest ever hero – Cú Chulainn.

Set on the North Coast, 'Sea-Burlin' tells how the iron prince danced his way across the Giant's Causeway to Scotland to meet his wife Morag. Of course, he wrestles all sorts of underwater monsters and a few uppity Fenians on his way, before coming back home to settle in Carrickfergus. Cue grand finale: "I wish I was…"

It ended to appalled silence. I haven't been so embarrassed since I was 13 and was caught playing air-guitar at a Showaddywaddy concert. Even the singing was pathetic – they'd tried to book Peter Corry, but he was washing his hair. Every night for a full year.

Danielle had come in from Greencastle for the concert, as a special treat. And she was most alarmed afterwards when I told her, deadpan, that we had just witnessed a dazzling display of her culture and heritage.

"If you marry Mommy, can I turn too?" she asked, almost serious for once.

"No need, honey," quipped Sue, "we're handing in our notice on Monday."

I left the pair of them back to the ranch after the show, and carried Danielle into the house, as she'd fallen asleep in the back. As I put her down on the couch, however, she woke up and whispered, "Mommy loves you too – she just doesn't want to tell you in case you run away."

And this, Dear Diary, is precisely why parents should not have children.

Tuesday, March 2

10.05am: Christ, Christ, this is bad.

Radio Foyle has just announced that Aileen Bates has been murdered. She was driving towards Dunavady, when a motorbike drew up beside her on the Drumbridge Road and a gunman shot her through the windscreen.

Chris Caddle, the mayor, has called an emergency meeting of the council for this afternoon.

Wednesday, March 3

I don't think I've ever been at such an angry gathering. Tony Blunt brought two off-duty cops with him as bodyguards, both tooled up. And it was just as well.

The gallery was packed with republicans – maybe 100 in all – all looking for an outlet for their grief and outrage.

I'd a brief chat with Caddle in his office before kick-off, and we agreed to try and take some of the steam out of things. But Tony Blunt couldn't keep his mouth shut. If anything, this morning's paper downplayed how bad it was, as the clipping shows:

BLUNT 'BLAMED' FOR BATES MURDER
By Stan Stevenson

Dunavady Council last night voted to censure DUP alderman Tony Blunt for "passively colluding" in yesterday's murder of Sinn Féin councillor Aileen Bates.

Sinn Féin proposed the sanction – which went through with the support of both the SDLP and independent councillor

Shay Gallagher – after Mr Blunt said he had been made aware of a possible attack on Ms Bates and had passed the details to the police. But the DUP man conceded that he had failed to warn his council colleague personally.

Ms Bates had been driving her son Seán, who is 15, to St Fiachra's College in Dunavady, when a blue Honda motorcycle pulled up beside her at roadworks a mile outside the town, and a pillion passenger shot her three times in the head with a pistol.

The 44-year-old councillor was rushed to Altnagelvin Hospital in Derry, but was dead on arrival. Her son was treated for shock and minor cuts caused by flying glass.

The Loyalist Action Group said they had carried out the attack and claimed the dead woman was a leading member of Cumann na mBan, the IRA's women's wing. This allegation has been strongly denied by her family.

The police arrested two Coleraine men yesterday afternoon, but legal sources say they expect them to be released later today. Lawyers and the PSNI have refused to confirm if the pair were the same men named by Ms Bates as the murderers of Sinn Féin Assembly candidate John 'Stumpy' O'Rourke.

In December, Ms Bates used chamber privilege to name Rex Stovell and Wilbur Townslow as her cousin's killers.

Uproar

At a stormy emergency meeting just hours after Ms Bates's death, a motion was passed to close all council services until after her funeral on Friday afternoon.

But there was uproar in the public gallery when Tony Blunt asserted that Aileen Bates could have been more careful and that "the world and his wife" knew her movements.

Mr Blunt sparked further booing and catcalls when he revealed that he himself had been contacted by a "concerned constituent" who had heard some "boys" talking about how she could be easily targeted doing the school run.

Mr Blunt said he had passed this information on to the police, but he didn't know if they'd alerted Ms Bates to the danger.

At this juncture, some republicans in the gallery stood up and started chanting: "You set her up, you set her up", and a bottle was thrown, which struck Mr Blunt on the shoulder.

The Sinn Féin council leader and current mayor, Chris Caddle, ordered the demonstrators to sit down or he'd put them out. And after a brief adjournment, the meeting continued, with Mr Caddle proposing the motion condemning the DUP man.

Councillors also voted to write letters to the security forces expressing no confidence in them and to the British government demanding an immediate end to Direct Rule.

An amendment by Shay Gallagher stressing that there should be absolutely no retaliation for the killings, and that anyone who knew the identity of the killers should tell the "proper authorities", was also adopted.

A UUP proposal – which stated that anyone with information on the murder should contact the local policing partnership – was defeated after Sinn Féin voted against it and Shay Gallagher abstained.

As this vote was taken, Tony Blunt cocked his finger and thumb in Mr Gallagher's direction and mouthed the words: "You're next."

• The PSNI said last night that they had no record of Mr Blunt alerting them to a threat to Ms Bates's life.

It was the first time since I've been in Dunavady that I've been frightened. You could taste the venom in the air.

How the hell did this happen? Three months ago, I was a French teacher whose only interest was getting drunk at the weekends. Today my friends are being murdered taking their children to school, and I'm next on the list.

You don't have to be schizophrenic to live here – but it helps.

Saturday, March 6
Spent most of today recovering from the funeral. It was the biggest I've seen since the hunger strikes – about 8,000 people were there in all.

All the nationalist councillors formed a guard of honour outside Drumbridge Parish Church, while the coffin was being taken inside. And fair play to Dexter Hart of the UUP, he walked past the cameras and into the chapel – defying a threat from his Orange lodge to kick him out if he attended. The bottom line, he said later, was that Aileen was his neighbour and had signed up to the same Agreement he had.

There was a tricolour over the coffin, but no paramilitary trappings, as the Shinners wanted to make the point that Aileen had never been a part of that.

Her son, Seán, stitches visible in his face, did the second reading – on the blessings of a mother's love. He was word perfect – clear, loud and proud. If you had closed your eyes for a minute, you would have sworn it was Aileen. There wasn't a dry eye in the house.

Fr Noel, I must say, also gave a masterful oration afterwards, praising Aileen's commitment to her family, her community and her country. He said she'd been murdered because she'd fought to get justice for her cousin, who'd been buried in the same graveyard just four months ago.

The only sour note was when a Special Branch photographer was spotted behind a wall, filming the interment. But he pulled back damn quickly when Barry Magee, a freelance for the Standard, went over and started taking pictures of him. The paper, fair play to them, published the cop's photo at the bottom of the front page this morning under the heading: VIOLATION.

As the funeral broke up, I fell in step with Tommy Bowtie and Fr Noel, and the three of us headed up to the parochial house, where we drank the best part of two bottles of Paddy before our host fell asleep.

We didn't talk a whole lot. You tend not to, when you're blotting it all out.

Monday, March 8
International Women's Day – must send Sue flowers.

The above entry, Diary, was unfortunately made some time ago and is now no longer valid.

Sue knew I was in bad old twist, so she arranged to come up to Derry yesterday to try and lift me out of it. But instead, we wound up fighting like cats in a bag and she stormed off.

It's my own fault; no doubt about it. I went to the shop for milk, and when I returned she had found my gold-stars book for the GWHs (under the mattress) and asked me what it was. She seemed to be in terrific form, smiling and joking about. And she'd travelled up from Greencastle to look after me. So, in a moment of sheer lunacy, I told her. What in under God was I thinking?

Sue, of course, immediately demanded to know where was her chart and how I would grade her against the two GWHs.

Even I was bright enough not to go there, but it was too late.

"You're a shallow bastard," she yelled. "Everybody from my mother, to my office workers, to half the damn Assembly warned me about you. But I didn't listen. I made a big leap for you, Shay. But I've just realised I'm wasting my time. You're not worth it."

I pleaded, told her I'd changed and that I have never loved anyone but her. I insisted that, no, I never had three women on the go at one time. And that since I'd met her I had been completely monogamous.

"So why are you holding on to your little jotter then?" she screamed as she marched for the door. "Posterity? Or are you just keeping your options open?"

It was terrible. Truly terrible. So terrible, that I don't think even Danielle's going to forgive me.

Tommy Bowtie – that walking beacon of sexual misery – says Sue is entirely justified.

"I can't believe you had an actual book – I thought it was all a cod," he said, when I rang him. "I warned you not to mess this girl about. You're not 12 years old any more."

"I'm a lot more mature than you are," I shouted, and slammed down the phone.

61

Friday, March 12

Last night's meeting of the District Policing Partnership was supposed to be a Q'n'A session with the local commander about the town's crime figures for the past year. The Shinner councillors don't attend the DPP events, of course, but their supporters do. So Superintendent Audrey Grafton barely had time to get her coat off before she started getting it in the teeth about police collusion in Aileen's murder.

Initially, the Super gave fairly bland, noncommittal answers to four separate questions from republicans about why the warning – if indeed there was a warning at all – hadn't been passed on. But when Fr Know-All accused her, quite rightly, of blowing smoke up all our backsides, she caved.

"Tell you what, so," said the Super, "let's go into closed session."

Now, as far as I'm aware, there is no provision for confidential business at DPP meetings. But the Super said she would answer the question as fully as she could if the press box and the public gallery were cleared.

So, after some to-ing and fro-ing, it was agreed that all clergy and political representatives – even those not on the DPP (i.e. me) – could stay on. And the 20 or so republicans in the main body of the hall eventually departed. Stan Stevenson from the Standard also left, muttering curses under his breath.

That left 12 of us in all, plus the Super.

"Okay," she said, when the back door was bolted, "this is what we know. We have no doubt that Rex Stovell and Wilbur Townslow from the self-styled Loyalist Action Group were behind the attack.

"The gun and the m.o. – three shots to the head – were the same as those used in the Stumpy O'Rourke shooting. And eye-witnesses, who saw the motorbike flying into Drumbridge after they shot Ms Bates, say the bike was being driven by a real pro. Stovell, you might know, is a fairly useful TT racer.

"But the same boys are very cunning and have managed to get themselves on CCTV footage filling a car with petrol at a Portrush garage at the exact time the shooting occurred. Don't know how they fixed it, but they did. Townslow runs the LAG website, and is pretty handy with computers, so it was probably him. But, for the moment, unless we can prove the tape's been doctored, they're untouchable."

Big Audrey also conceded that there had been eyewitnesses who put both men at Stumpy's murder, but who had subsequently retracted their statements.

"I can also privately confirm," she continued, "that I am recommending an internal inquiry into Special Branch's investigations of both killings.

"Tony Blunt, it seems, did indeed pass on a warning to an officer in the Branch, who, for whatever reason, decided not to alert other departments – including me. And just by the way, I would appreciate it if the council would withdraw its 'collusion' allegation against Mr Blunt, in case some nut-job would have a go at him next.

"There was also a warning about the O'Rourke murder, which likewise wasn't passed on. So, to cut to the chase, yes, we are looking at the possibility that someone in the service – the Branch – is running both Stovell and Townslow.

"I would like to assure you, however, that whenever we find whoever is doing this, we'll throw the book at them."

Sunday, March 14

Yesterday's Derry Standard carried a full front-page exclusive report on the DPP meeting under the heading: SPECIAL BRANCH RUNNING AILEEN'S KILLERS, SAYS PSNI CHIEF. Most of the Sundays – Irish and British alike – have picked up on it this morning and are using it as a stick to lash the slow pace of police reform.

Audrey Grafton must be spitting tacks.

Thankfully, there were enough of us in the room, so she'll never be sure who did the leaking to the Standard – unless they start checking phone records.

Good job I rang from Fr Know-All's, so, while he was out in the jacks.

Wednesday, March 17, St Patrick's Day

I've no party machine to pay for me to go to Washington, so as soon as Tommy Bowtie arrives I'm for the hostelries of Main Street, Dunavady.

Here at least, you're guaranteed first-class genuine trad music – none of your Phil Coulter versions – black and white stout as God made it, and you'll not have to look at another damn politician, as they're all over doing the Stage-Paddy bit in the States.

This morning's Derry Standard, meanwhile, is still trumpeting its success in breaking the DPP story. But at the top of page three, I see a bit of revisionism creeping in:

ALDERMAN ANTHONY BLUNT: AN APOLOGY

In last week's Derry Standard, it was reported that, during a debate on the murder of Aileen Bates, Alderman Blunt cocked his finger and thumb at Shay Gallagher MLA and mouthed the words: "You're next."

We accept entirely, Mr Blunt's assertion that he merely gestured with his finger – in an ordinary non-threatening fashion – towards Mr Gallagher and said the words: "You're <u>nuts.</u>"

We apologise unreservedly to Mr Blunt for the distress and embarrassment caused to him by our genuine mistake. We have agreed to pay him substantial damages and make a similar payment to the Police Widows Fund.

We also accept that Mr Blunt passed on a warning about Ms Bates's murder to the police and that the PSNI's assertion that he hadn't done so was incorrect.

I was sitting six feet away from Blunt. And I still can see him pretending to blow gun smoke off the top of his index finger.

He set up Aileen Bates, sure as apples. The paper caved far too easily.

So I rang the Standard and spoke to Stan Stevenson and offered to sign an affidavit saying Blunt threatened me. But as far as Stan's concerned, it's over.

"There's not a person in this town who'll believe our apology," said Stan. "We've exposed Blunt for what he is. And he's going to need all that money to put armour-plating round his house for when the boys in the balaclavas come visiting. I just hope they take me along with them to watch."

Friday, March 19

Got an e-mail from King Size Barkley announcing that Tony Blunt has been found dead in a brothel in Rome, disguised as a Catholic priest.

You scroll down the message, and it continues: "Carlsberg don't do e-mails, but if they did…"

I sent it on to Stan Stevenson to cheer him up. And I also forwarded it to Sue Mack in the hope of breaking a little ice. But it appears I've now worked my way onto her 'Block Senders' list.

Monday, March 22

Danielle rang me last night to give me a hard time for making Mommy so miserable. It was my first communication back from that part of the world in a full week despite about a dozen phone-calls and as many e-mails.

"Personally, I don't see the harm in the gold stars," she said. "We have them at school – it helps you keep score and lets you know who's the best. So I told Mommy this."

"And what did Mommy say?"

"She said that gold stars are grand when you're my age, but when you hit your mid-twenties they're very insulting. And particularly when you read the list of what you get the stars for."

Note to self: never write anything down. Ever again.

"She didn't tell you what was on the list?"

"No, she said I wasn't old enough – and would never be old enough."

"So, how do I get her to forgive me?" I asked.

"Problem is, Shay, you're not serious enough for her. She has good fun with you – but then again, so do I, and I'm nine. You have to make her feel special. And besides, she has a new boyfriend."

"So what's he like?" I pressed.

"Well," said Danielle, "he's a big Proddy numptie, who was at school with her and has been chasing her since she was about 14.

"We all went to the pictures on Friday night. And I asked him if he was going to be my new daddy. So he – the big lube – said, 'That depends on your mother.' Mommy then spilt her

65

drink all over herself, and when we got home, she sent me straight to my room.

"Can't say you've much to worry about there. But if there's any danger I'll give you a call. I like having you about, Shay. Mommy's always in better form – even if you are a no-good Fenian flake."

Thursday, March 25

Things got back to normal, more or less, at last night's council meeting when we got to fight over something other than one of our number being whacked and another helping out in the whacking.

Derry City Council have asked other local authorities in the county to weigh in behind their motion to have the title 'Londonderry' struck off the books.

It's not so much of an issue up here in Dunavady, as we actually use the Irish form 'Condae an Dhoire' on all our letterheads. But it allowed us to talk about anything but the war.

The vote was only going to go one way in our chamber but the Shinners and Stoops quite generously afforded the unionist bloc quite a bit of time to jump up and down and vent their anger at the 'injustice' of it all.

Then, however, Tony Blunt asked if we could amend the proposal and the teabags hit the fan. Blunt said the motion should note the "concerns" of the Protestant community over the change and acknowledge that republican "scorched earth" policies were directly responsible for provoking recent reactionary attacks by the "misguided" Loyalist Action Force. Subtext: Aileen Bates got what was coming to her.

Chris Caddle's face lit up in a fury and he was up out of his chairman's seat before the Town Clerk could hold him back. He lunged at Blunt, two tables away, but Dexter Hart, who was a useful scrumhalf, grabbed Chris by his waist and pinned him to his desk.

So instead, Chris cocked his finger and thumb very deliberately at Tony Blunt and repeatedly shouted over the melee: "You're next – you're next." He then turned his head to Stan Stevenson, who was alone in the press box, and, still spitting froth, panted: "For the record, I would like it noted that I pointed at Alderman Blunt and told him he would be next. I'll do it with my own hands."

Well, Stan Stevenson who is quite a decent guy in spite of his obvious shortcoming, closed his notebook, put his pen down on the table in front of him and stared, pointedly, from Blunt to Caddle and back again.

I took my cue from Stan and immediately proposed that the events of the past five minutes should be excised from the record. Dexter Hart, who still had a giant bear-paw on Chris Caddle's throat, seconded, and the motion went through on the nod.

Sometimes it's important to remember the living as well as the dead.

•••••••

They missed the point of what Blunt was at entirely. He was a lot more astute than they were giving him credit for. They were so wrapped up trying to get someone to blame that they couldn't see he was winding them all up to take the bad look off his own lot.

No doubt about it, both Shay and Chris Caddle let Aileen's killing cloud their judgement. Whose agenda did her death serve? Certainly not Blunt's. He was way too isolated in Dunavady to be starting a war.

Blaming him for the murder was dense. He'd nothing to do with it. Audrey Grafton told them that herself at the DPP meeting. And that was another Gallagher brainstorm — leaking the whole collusion plot to the press. Just what everybody wanted, two loose cannons like Stovell and Townslow in a state of panic.

Then again, as Shay said, three months previously he was just a French teacher and part-time lush. Politics has a damn steep learning curve. And occasionally, it has one bastard of a sudden dip.

APRIL 2004

Sue, I hate to say it, had been a calming influence on Shay. And apparently, he'd been good for her too. I suppose, if nothing else, he's always useful for a bit of levity. But for my money, Sue warranted a lot more than that.

I talked to Fr Know-All about their break-up, and surprisingly, he suggested keeping the lines to Sue open through Frank the Tank. Fr K thought it was important to stabilise Shay — even with a Protestant. Maybe he was hoping to claim bonus points with God by converting her. I don't know. I didn't think it was a good idea.

Shay, it had become apparent, wasn't very good with rejection — particularly for a man who'd handed out more than his fair share. And he started wandering round like a man looking for an accident. Though, fair play to him, he just about trebled his chances of disaster by binge-drinking as well.

•••••••

Friday, April 2

An English journalist called into the office today to get my reaction to the publication of the Cory Report into state murder here. Or at least that's what he said he was doing.

The guy, whose card introduced him as Emile Rees from some ITN Special Programmes unit, was about 40, massively tall, Oxbridge-educated from his accent, and attempting to dress down by wearing a grubby mac.

I buzzed out to Frank at the front desk to hold my calls for exactly ten minutes, giving 'Emile' his deadline. So he took the hint and got stuck in right away.

Emile wanted to know if Dunavady Council would now be calling for a public inquiry into Aileen Bates's killing because of collusion. Now, we've pretty much done that already, and I told that to Emile. But given that the government are still frustrating Cory's demand for an inquiry into Pat Finucane's killing, I said I wouldn't hold my breath. The Finucanes have been waiting 15 years.

Terribly-civilised Emile then asked me, very much off the record, if there were those "within the community" who would be happy enough with a "private" settlement to the Bates killing.

I asked him what he meant. So he suggested that there mightn't be many tears shed locally, if the gunmen who shot Aileen and Stumpy, were themselves found toes up in a country field.

I raised my hand to start objecting. But before I could open my mouth, from inside his jacket Emile produced an envelope, which I could see contained a floppy disk, and he placed it on my desk.

He stared at me with very professional, cold, dead eyes, until I stilled myself.

"This," he said, "is everything we've got on Rex Stovell and Wilbur Townslow. What they've done, where they frequent, their handlers in Special Branch, all their LAG associates, and, most importantly for you, what they're planning next.

"This disc, I would warn you, is confidential material that is of use to terrorists. If you are caught with it, you could go to jail for a long time. So don't think of going public.

"If you don't want it, no offence taken. I'll be on my way and you'll never see me again. I assure you that I am not wasting your time – nor is this a set-up."

But of course it was a set-up. So I gestured to the envelope without touching it and told him to take it away.

"I'll have no part of this," I insisted. "But of course, if an unmarked disc arrives in an unmarked envelope in my letterbox any time soon, I'll have to check it out and see what's on it…"

Big Emile grinned he understood, and announced, "Jolly good," as he headed for the door.

"Why are you doing this?" I asked him as he put his hand on the knob.

"Pour encourager les autres," he laughed. "That's French for 'we're cancelling all our freelances'. But you'll know that, naturally – given you teach the subject.

"One more point," he said. "Tony Blunt loathes these guys. Sure, sometimes, he has to pander to the mob. But when it comes to the dirty stuff, he bats for the goodies. He wasn't threatening you with Stovell and Townslow – he was warning you to watch out for them."

And with that, Emile swung his dirty mac over his arm and ducked out under my six-foot-six doorframe.

Saturday, April 3

Drove out to the office and, sure enough, there in the letterbox was an unmarked disk inside an unmarked envelope.

Called Tommy Bowtie, who advised me to pass it on to him and ask no more questions.

"But shouldn't I report it?" I asked him.

"Who to?" he replied.

"What about ITN?" I suggested. "I mean, they're bound to have a separate non-spying wing?"

"I suppose it's possible," laughed Tommy. "After all, the IRA have a totally independent political wing…

"The bottom line, Shay, is that everyone's a spy. The problem comes when you have to figure out who they work for."

But he's right about the disc – I don't want to know. So I popped the little package into another envelope and dropped it into Tommy's office mailbox, marked Eyes Only.

Tuesday, April 6

Tony Blunt reckons things have been too peaceful here for the last couple of weeks, so at tonight's council meeting he'll be proposing that Dunavady should follow the fine example set by Ballymena last week and award Ian Paisley the Freedom of the Borough.

Personally, I reckon there's more chance of the Big Man being asked to sing Amhrán na bhFiann at the All-Ireland Final, but it should be an interesting evening all the same. The Shinners and Stoops have put down amendments as have the UUP.

Talking of uptight, thickheaded planters, Sue left a message with Frank the Tank to say that she wants to call off our pairing arrangement. That is, our official Stormount one. She told him that she's in talks to rejoin the UUP and wanted to give me a month's notice to quit.

Sue also warned Frank to be very careful about opening my mail, as she heard he was a nice guy – and I'm certainly not worth it. Frank offered to put her through to me, but she told him, and I quote, "I'd sooner let David Blunkett give me a bikini wax."

So things are looking up there then.

Thursday, April 8

Most of yesterday was spent in the back office with the curtain drawn, choking back Alka Seltzer and guilt in equal measure.

Somewhat unwisely, I went on the skite in the Castle Inn with both the Shinners and the Stoops after Tuesday night's meeting. The Shinners were celebrating the result – more of which anon. And the Stoops were introducing the new press officer for their Drumbridge office, Mary Naughton – a high-flying politics graduate from Trinity, who spent two years working with a congressman in Denver. Mary is also warm, sweet, charming and a double for Danii Minogue (apart from D's dodgy nose). But like all true heroines, she has a tragic flaw. Well, actually she has two – one, she has a shocking temper, or so she tells me; and two, she's a rotten judge of character.

And, yes, they forgot to warn her about me...

Suffice it to say that by teatime yesterday, the SDLP had formally broken all relations with both Fianna Fáil and myself. And Mary and her cousin Packie, the councillor, spent the evening driving up and down Main Street with a loaded tranquilliser gun and two tethering ropes. Frank, bless his socks, got me out the back door and took me home via the back road to Drumbridge.

Old Uncle Shay would not have approved at all – despite his own reputation as a ladies man. A dog can't help being a dog, he would always say – but a smart one won't bite holes in next-door's sheep. The front page of this morning's Standard didn't do me many favours either:

ADAMS, DEV TO BE MADE FREEMEN
By Stan Stevenson

Gerry Adams is not – and has never been – a member of the IRA, Dunavady councillors affirmed on Tuesday night.

The independent nationalist Shay Gallagher joined with Sinn Féin members to vote down a DUP bid to confer Ian Paisley with the freedom of the Borough. But an amendment, proclaiming both Mr Adams and the late Eamon DeValera as freemen, was carried – as was a rider "accepting entirely" the Sinn Féin president's recent claims that he had only ever been involved in non-military politics.

Speaking after the vote, SF council leader Chris Caddle asserted: "This proves beyond doubt that Gerry was never in the 'Ra, and we hope the government and securocrats will take note.

"He is as pure and innocent as the Colombia Three."

But the DUP's Tony Blunt said the decision was "ridiculous", "beggared belief" and "insulted" the entire council chamber.

To which Cllr. Caddle replied: "But, Blunty, you started it – you and your craic about Big Ian."

An SDLP amendment to have John Hume also declared a freeman was shelved due to lack of time, though the council did vote to thank him again for setting up the Credit Union.

But a Dexter Hart proposal to offer the keys of the Borough to David Trimble failed when his two UUP colleagues refused to second the motion. Both men had voted against Mr Trimble during last week's No Confidence motion at the party's Council meeting. A source close to one of them told the Derry Standard last night: "Trimble can beat his 60 percent up his h***."

A second DUP motion, to declare Jeffrey Donaldson 'The High King of Foreglen', did have better luck, however. Though SF amended it to 'The Not Very Tall Lord of Drumbridge'.

Lord Donaldson has yet to disclose if he will be taking up this ancient title, which includes the right to drive sheep through AOH parades and to burn at the stake any witch caught on his land.

"Barbie had better mind where she goes on the Euro campaign," commented Tony Blunt.

Honour
Meanwhile, there was considerable surprise when the former Irish Taoiseach and President, Eamon DeValera, became the first dead person to be made a freeman of the Borough.

But Shay Gallagher – who is linked to Fianna Fáil – said that the title was a largely honorary one that Mr DeValera was unlikely to be using.

"We would have given the award to Bertie," explained Gallagher, "except there's a better chance of Dev coming here to collect it himself."

• The Derry Standard can exclusively reveal that, after Tuesday's meeting, Shay Gallagher held "feverish" talks with the SDLP's press office with a view to a short term FF-SDLP merger. Insiders say, however, that the talks collapsed in "spectacular" fashion yesterday.

What a low-down, dirty dog you are, Stan.

Friday, April 9
Good Friday – a fine day for a crucifixion.

An e-mail arrives from Sue and she's obviously read the Standard: "Didn't take you long, did it, you snake?"

Sent her one back: "Didn't think you cared…"

Thirty seconds later, her retort dinged in: "Don't flatter yourself – I don't."

"Well that's all right then," I replied. "And anyway, Danielle tells me you're almost engaged."

"Yeah, but did she tell you he's a police inspector?"

"Really? Well, I hope you have a long, boring Protestant life together."

"We will," she concluded. "Bite my arse."

Oh Sacré Mère de Merde. A cop. I think I'd better rebore my entire computer and sort out those drinking-on fines. Just in case.

Sunday, April 11

As a non-party nationalist, I'm normally spared the Easter Sunday commemorations, but Tommy Bowtie reckoned it would be a good idea for me to show my face at the North Derry rally this morning, out of respect for Aileen and Stumpy.

I suppose at least it was one spot I wasn't going to run into Mary Naughton and crazy cousin Packie. I sent Mary a bunch of flowers on Friday to apologise; lilies – women read far too much into roses. And I scribbled a little note explaining how I'm still in trauma from a major break-up and I'm sorry she got involved. It's a line I've used before with a fair degree of success, and this time there may even be some truth in it.

Thank God for David Beckham and Rebecca Loos all over the Sunday papers to take the bare look off me. (Note to self – beware the dangers of unprotected text.)

After the wreath-laying in the graveyard, we had an excruciating 27 MINUTES of Chris Caddle's thoughts on the political stalemate. Stan Stevenson, who was hiding his hangover behind a pair of Raybans, didn't even take his jotter out of his pocket.

"Don't you want to take some notes?" I asked him.

"What – and egg him on to talk even longer?" snapped back Stan. "He's getting two paragraphs, same as last year: the deadlock is bad, blah, blah; and it's everybody else's fault bar us."

After the rally, it was off to the Parochial House for a spot of lunch with Fr Know-All, and the discussion was on Blair's new proposal for three days of 'hothouse' talks at the end of the month.

The room erupted when Fr K, who misses nothing, asked me, "Will you be going along to these talks yourself, Shay, or are you going to use your pair?"

"I'm not sure of Ms McEwan's intentions as of this date, Father," I told him deadpan.

"Indeed," smirked my old boss, who's obviously been talking to Tommy Bowtie. "And exactly what part of 'Bite my arse' is it that you don't understand? Never mind, maybe you could go along to the talks with the SDLP delegation."

This again provoked much merriment and snorting. "Father, you'll forgive me for saying this," I replied, "but did you ever think of becoming a policeman instead of a priest?"

"I did indeed," laughed Fr K. "In fact, I even had my application in. But sadly, they rejected me…"

"Too short?" I sniffed.

"No," he countered, "they found out my parents were married."

Later, on the way back into Derry, I asked Tommy Bowtie was there anything interesting on the floppy disc from big Emile the Spy.

"What disc?" he grinned and tapped his nose furtively.

Yep, if today had a theme, it would have been 'Wind up your local MLA'.

Sunday, April 18

The office has been closed for the week on account of the holidays and the excessive drinking.

Spent an hour reading the Sundays to get back up to speed today – and you get the sense that the Euro elections are well and truly underway. Michael McDowell is pulling the Shinners' pigtails and accusing them of links to criminals at Dublin docks. And there's a lot of speculation about the Independent Monitoring Commission's report into the ceasefires, which is due out later in the week.

But it's the Sunday Independent which wins the No-Holds-Barred Headline of the Week award with: IRA BASTARD ARMIES ARE A BLOODY, TREASONOUS MAFIA. All they were missing was a picture of a naked hooker.

Tuesday, April 20

The DUP have announced a new way to settle the Derry name dispute once and for all. They'll organise a team of unionists to take on a team of nationalists at any sport of their choosing, except all those games that used to bar the Crown Forces from playing, i.e. anything we're good at.

But Chris Caddle, who's always up for a challenge, contacted Tony Blunt to say he's on – so long as it's not baseball. (Chris, for one, can think far enough ahead to work out what the photo would be the next time there's a punishment battering on his patch.)

Blunt then suggested rugby, but most of our lot wouldn't know the rules and besides, Dexter Hart is still too useful. Likewise cricket's out, because of the risk of injury all round.

So it looks as though a soccer match could settle the fate of Stroke City – as long as we can get a date on everyone's calendar.

Thursday, April 22

The governments have cancelled next week's hothouse talks and fined the Shinners a small post office (£120K) for minor breaches of the ceasefire.

But the good news is that everyone now has a free space in their diary on Saturday night, so the Grand Name Change cup final is going to be held under the floodlights at the Brandywell.

The bad news is, I'm in the starting line-up. And, thanks to the '22-percent rule' set down by the Equality Commission, so is Mary Naughton.

Course, it's only a friendly…

Sunday, April 25

We should have known we were in for a fight when the Londonderry XI ruled out our suggestion of John Alderdice of the Alliance Party for referee on the grounds that he has a 'Fenian-looking' beard.

Instead, they demanded Billy Hutchinson, insisting that no-one in their right mind, Orange or Green, is going to go nose-to-nose with him over a decision. (Well, at least no-one's ever done it before.)

Then, just prior to kick-off, I got my second rude surprise, when I looked down at their subs' bench, and who was stretching out her beautiful long legs only Sue McEwan.

"She's our secret weapon," grinned Tony Blunt at me. "Anyone who scores for us gets a long snog at the dance afterwards."

"It'll be a short queue," I sniped back. "Though if you get

there, be sure and ask her for me if she's got rid of that nasty little rash."

"Didn't you hear?" retorted Blunt. "She sent him back to Dunavady with his tail between his legs."

So much for the pleasantries. I decided to go over to say a quick hello to Danielle who was in the New Stand carrying a placard that read, 'Where would we be without London?'

"That's an easy one," I said pointing at the sign. "Dublin."

"Mommy made me hold it," she sighed.

"Where's your new daddy?" I asked, giving her a conspiratorial grin.

"He couldn't make it tonight, thank God," she laughed. "He's out with the river bailiff catching poachers."

"As long as he remembers to throw the little ones back," I quipped. But it went right over her head.

"He's warming up a little, though," said Danielle. "But I still have to hide my DVDs whenever he comes in. And I have to take the chip off the NTL box, so I can't watch my cartoons. But Nana says he sure as hell beats the alternative."

"What about Mommy?" I pressed.

"Well, she wants you to know that she's madly in love, and looking at an October wedding. She also said to tell you she's out house-hunting, and is planning to give me a little brother or sister very soon."

"Can't abide him, so?" I suggested.

"Knocks back half a bottle of gin before she steps out the door with him," laughed Danielle. "Wish to hell she'd give me some too. We've been to the Folk Park four times already this month. Mommy says he's the only man ever thrown out of the Free Ps for being too dull."

I wouldn't say it was a rough match, but it's never a good sign when the Knights of Malta run out of stretchers. Even Billy Hutchinson winced at some of the tackles. The game was barely 30 seconds old when the two centre halves exchanged hellos, resulting in five staples for Frank the Tank on his left eyebrow and an ambulance to ER for Dexter Hart.

Five minutes later, the casualty lists were level when Chris Caddle was coldcocked after attempting to nutmeg Tony Blunt. Blunt caught him with an elbow in the temple on the ref's blind side and didn't even get a warning. Chris even got to share the ride to X-ray with Dexter.

Mary Naughton of the Derry XI then picked up the first booking of the day, when she was cautioned for calling David Ervine a "baldy Hun". Hutch wielded the yellow card in defence of his old PUP mate on the grounds that it was "a sectarian comment" – oh, and Big Davy supports Liverpool, not Rangers. Mary protested that it wasn't a "Hun" she called Davy, but to no avail.

Five minutes from half time, we took the lead thanks to a defensive mix-up. A high ball came in from the right, and Mildred Garfield in nets called on Mike McGimpsey to leave the ball. McGimpsey, however, said we've left too damned much to the DUP already, and the pair clattered into one another. This allowed me to nip in and square the ball to Frank the Tank, who tapped in from the six-yard line. Smart play by my good self, but it'll be Frank and his Braveheart scar getting all the headlines.

Shortly after the break, it was level. Sue McEwan, who'd come on at half-time, went up for a corner and wound up with a fist in her nose. The ref consulted his linesman and immediately red-carded Mary Naughton. Mary had no argument, but she hit the still prostrate Sue a boot in the ribs before being dragged from the pitch. Apprentice Boy Willie Hay then came up and dispatched the penalty, after the Parades Commission overruled protests that it wasn't his traditional route.

Ten minutes later, however, and Frank the Tank forced the decider. In true GAA fashion, he shouldered, clawed and bit his way past four Londonderry defenders before firing a thunderous shot towards the goal. The ball was actually going wide, but at the last second ricocheted off the side of John Dallat's head and spun into the net. Happily, the SDLP man was only unconscious for a few minutes and quickly woke up to claim the goal.

After the final whistle went, Gregory said they'd be lodging an appeal against the result as Frank the Tank wasn't a paid-up party officer, and shouldn't have been on the field. But the whole exercise was worth it if only for the picture in this morning's Standard of me on the sideline, wiping the blood off Sue Mack's nose. Stan Stevenson, the bad article, gave it the heading: THE TRUE MEANING OF SPORT. Clearly, Stan didn't hear Sue telling me that as soon as she gets better, she's going to rip off my little Taig girlfriend's arms and beat me round Dunavady with them.

●●●●●●●

Emile, I reckon, was the final warning. It's bad when even the spooks come in and tell you to mind yourself. There was no way I was letting Shay see the files though. He'd only have gone for the quick headline and would have wound up dead within a week.

Needless to say, he didn't want to hand the disc over — but I bullied him into it. It was like that scene from A Few Good Men when Jack Nicholson roars at Tom Cruise: "You can't handle the truth." Except, of course, Shay's a lot better looking than Tom, and I drink more than Jack.

Everybody was getting a little frayed so it was great to have the football match to lower the temperature. And Fr Know-All and myself were able to do a bit of chair-shuffling at the dinner afterwards to ensure that Mary Naughton was able to sit beside Frank the Tank, hero of the hour. And by the time the night was over, that was one less thing Shay had to worry about.

MAY 2004

Shay never fully grasped how angry the LAG were about Sue. But the longer the year went on, the more worried I was becoming. It didn't help that I'd read Emile's disc and that one of the predictions — a fairly hefty robbery in Garvagh — had already come about. Their plans for Shay were in there as well, though there was no way I was going to tell him the extent of them. He'd never have slept.

Emile was right. It would have been much easier to be proactive and hand the disc over to Chris Caddle. There was enough in there for his old pals to hunt down Stovell and Townslow and punch their clocks. But I couldn't do it. Maybe the law's the last thing left that I believe in.

Instead, I took to briefing Shay day and night about his personal security. But like always, it went in one ear, around the big wooden spike in the middle of his head, and out the other.

The rest of my time was spent keeping Shay out of mischief during the European election campaigning. The Stoops and the Shinners were both lobbying him heavily — they figured he could have been worth a couple of thousand votes to them. Though I must say, Shay's quite the master at not committing himself — it's a habit that was bound to come in useful one day.

•••••••

Thursday, May 6

It's been open house at the office this week as all the Euro canvassers drop in to bitch about their candidates. Because I'm not involved in the fight, the troops feel free to open up without feeling too disloyal.

The SDLP are the hardest pressed. They know from the Assembly elections in November that their man Martin Morgan is in line for a tanking – and to make matters worse, it's their first Euro poll without Hume.

Packie Naughton is back speaking to me, ever since Mary

hooked up with Frank the Tank after the Name Change match. And he called in yesterday for a coffee and to re-open a few approach roads.

"Martin is a lovely fella," he said, "but it's next to impossible to sell a Belfast accent in this part of the country. Derry people get a pain in their head listening to anyone west of the Bann. We think they're all smart mouths, and they think we're all culchies. It's the same reason the Derry Shinners all love McGuinness and can't abide, well, pick a number.

"Our other difficulty is that John Gilliland is going to hoover up some of the Catholic farmer votes here in the west, even if he is a Prod. Bottom line, if this were a regular job they were all going for, Gilliland's the only one who'd get an interview…"

The Gilliland pitch, of course, was just a curve ball Packie was throwing at me to find out which way I'd be swinging come Election Day. He's obviously heard the talk that a few high rankers in Fianna Fáil are interested in recruiting Mr G, who's a former farmers' leader and very well connected. So, to put poor Packie's mind at rest, I assured him that I'd be giving his man my number one – just as I intend to blithely lie to every other campaigner who bangs on my window.

Next in was a glum-looking Dexter Hart, who wanted to make sure that I'd give the UUP's Jim Nicholson a higher preference than the DUP's Jim Allister.

"Don't worry," I laughed. "I always vote from the Least Evil down."

"Jim'll keep the seat," said Dexter, "though the way we've been tearing the party apart, we hardly deserve it. People are quick to work out that the governments don't give a damn about the UUP any more. All they care about is getting the DUP and Sinn Féin on the one page.

"Our people gave away too much to end the war, and we're getting punished. But looking back, we were just doing the DUP's work by proxy. Now the dirty business is done, Robinson and Co can step in and hold things up for a couple of years before claiming all the glory. But, the truth is, it's already over. And the only way it's heading now is for Big Ian or Little Pete to hold out his hand to Hairy Gerry."

Dexter was barely out the door, when Tony Blunt popped in to ask for "a decent preference". Though they'll hardly need it.

"Who's Jim Allister anyway?" I asked him.

"Well, he's not Paisley Junior for a start," he grinned.

"Okay, so," I replied. "He has my number eight."

"Nor is he Maurice Morrow," laughed Blunt.

"Okay," I relented, "my number seven, so."

"But there's only seven candidates."

"Well, that would be about right, then."

Finally, this morning, I had the Shinners in, canvassing for Bairbre. And Chris Caddle is finding that his old-school credentials count for little in the new politically-correct dispensation.

"Keep this to yourself," he said, "but we're scared to death of her. In the pub after the Ard Comhairle meetings, I'm afraid to get drunk any more. It's like saying 'Fuck' in front of a nun.

"Problem is, she's very, very clever – far too clever a doll for me. In fairness, she's perfect for Europe. She's fluent in Spanish and Irish, and is probably the only person I know who has read the European Constitution from end to end. But best of all, when we get her out of the country, I might finally get my nose inside the new lap-dancing club on Parnell Square."

The Shinners, however, know that Bairbre is home in a boat – even if Chris will be barred from the victory party.

Tuesday, May 11

Was going to ring Sue Mack to invite her to the Mayor's Ball but lost my nerve. So instead, I got King Size Barkley to call her and pretend to be the man from NTL.

"It's about your TV account, Miss McEwan," he began in a very posh voice. "We understand that you're paying for our basic package?"

"That's right," replied Sue, "about 14 quid a month."

"But the problem is," continued King Size, "our new technology shows that your line has actually been chipped – that is, tampered with – for the last six months, to give you free access to an additional £35 a month worth of programming."

"I don't know what you're talking about," Sue lied.

"We've also got an independent witness," said King Size, "a police inspector no less, who says the NTL box has definitely been interfered with."

"You've the wrong house," insisted Sue. "Come and take the damn thing out – I'll get Sky."

"Not that simple, Miss McEwan," said Barkley, "there's a back payment of £210 plus interest, plus vat. And, of course, the £500 fine for damaging our equipment."

"You're joking," said Sue starting to panic a little. "It's Shay Gallagher again, isn't it?"

"I assure you this is no joke, Miss McEwan – if you don't pay the fine within a fortnight, you'll get a summons to appear at Omagh Magistrates Court."

"But I'm a single mother," protested Sue. "And all I want to do is add a little colour to my poor nine-year-old daughter's life. Is there nothing you can do for me?"

"Impossible," said King Size, sounding more and more like a Law Lord. "Oh, on second thoughts, it's just possible there's one thing you could do…"

"Name it," declared Sue.

"Well," said King Size, "is it true you like a bit of Fenian rough…?"

According to Danielle, who was in on it, Sue slammed the phone so hard into its cradle that she smashed the glass table. And no, she doesn't think there's anyway Mommy will be going to the dance with me now.

Saturday, May 15

Wound up at the Ball in spite of myself last night. Chris Caddle, the outgoing mayor, promised me that there would be lots of fresh young talent at the Holiday Inn – so proving once and for all that you should never set your standards by a Shinner.

I actually offered my ticket to Frank the Tank, but he was already going as Mary Naughton's chaperone. So there was nothing for it but to go and sit at the top table like a big lonely snotter.

They make a very handsome couple, Frank and Mary. He's a lot more confident since he struck up with her – talking more, arguing more. And his relaxed nature seems to have done wonders for her psychotic edge. Indeed, for the first time since I met her, I felt comfortable in her company when she'd a knife in her hand.

Chris punctuated his speech with digs at all the other parties, and in particular the Dups, who didn't turn up. "Tony Blunt sends his apologies," he declared. "He says the bomb under the top table was supposed to go off five minutes ago..."

And there was no escape for me, either. "I see Shay Gallagher's dance card is empty tonight," said the mayor. "As you know, he and Sue McEwan had brought a whole new meaning to the phrase 'getting their teeth into Strand One'. But Sue isn't at all happy since she found out Shay's been sitting on an All-Ireland body..."

Much chortling from the masses and some sucking in of air from Father Know-All. I flicked my eyebrows "sorry" in Frank's direction, but he just shrugged back "what do I care?"

Later, when I was satisfied that the night had no saving graces, I decided it was time to work the room and go home. A real politician, as Uncle Shay told me many times, will never leave a function until he's shaken the hand of every man in the hall and told every woman how lovely her new hairdo's looking. It's your job; it's who you are – pure and simple. Not everyone you talk to is going to buy it, but everyone you ignore is a lost vote.

I had just stopped at the Stoops' table, when Stan Stevenson swung by and spotted Frank with his hand on Mary's shoulder. The mischievous little sod then asked me if Fianna Fáil and the SDLP were opening up a merger on a new front. I was about to make a smart remark and not answer him, when Frank decided to have a go for himself.

"Let's face it, if the SDLP don't tie in with the South, they're finished," he said, in full serious mode. "Six County-only politics is dead; look at the Alliance Party. The unionists know how important it is to pitch in at Westminster – they wound up with John Major in their pocket for five years. So it's about time we started taking our case – and our voting weight – to Leinster House. Northerners need a voice in the Dáil, and the Southern Irish need their authority felt at Stormont."

Pity Frank missed the obvious – which is that Bertie and his Republican Party would sooner poke their eyes out with cocktail sticks than give Northerners a foothold in the South. But there's no doubt about it, Frank is keeping a very close eye on how things are moving and is going to be hard to stop when he gets on the ballot in a few years time. And judging by the looks Mary Naughton's giving him, she intends to be around to see it. Wonder was I a little hasty there…?

Thursday, May 20

The Annual North Derry Triathlon takes place on Sunday and I've been asked to fire the starting pistol. Frank the Tank is actually taking part in the event which involves a seven-mile run from Dunavady to Drumbridge, 60 lengths in the pool there, and a 30-mile cycle from Drumbridge to Garvagh and back over the mountain into Dunavady.

I briefly considered doing the shorter duathlon for charity. But Tommy Bowtie, who called into the office yesterday, strongly advised me not to. It seems he's very spooked about my security. I asked him was this about Emile's disc, and this time he didn't try to laugh it off. He just acknowledged there's a serious threat on my life and that it's possible they might try something this weekend.

I inquired if there were any of the Stoops or the Shinners being targeted, but surprisingly he shook his head. "No. It's you they want," said Tommy. "You've committed the cardinal sin of violating one of their number, and they're going to make you pay for it."

"This is about Sue Mack?" I asked, not really believing him.

"She's a Proddy icon," he replied, grim as death. "As far as they're concerned, you're a stain on her character. So, on Sunday morning, just fire the starting gun, get into my car and spend the rest of the day drinking the bit out on west-bank Derry, like you always do. They're not going to come into the city to get you – it's too far from friendly turf. And on Monday, we'll look about getting you a full-time bodyguard."

"Sure don't I already have Frank?" I countered.

"Frank is far too bright and far too useful to you to be putting his neck on the line," said Tommy.

"What about you, so?" I grinned. "That belly of yours would stop an RPG."

"No," he said. "Much though I'd love to, my wife would only tell me I was taking the easy way out. We're going to get you a vicious thug – pure and simple. No teeth, no hair, and tattoos up and down his arm. A guy who'll shoot first and ask questions later."

"An ex-cop then," I quipped. And we both laughed to let a little steam out.

Monday, May 24

SCUM. SCUM. FUCKING SCUM.

Tommy Bowtie was right. The bastards did come for me. But they couldn't get me because I was drinking the bit out back in west-bank Derry.

So instead, they waited until Frank the Tank was four miles from the finishing line in Dunavady and blew half his chest away with a shotgun. They then used the second barrel to blow his brains out, just to be sure.

The only way Mary Naughton could identify him was from the triathlon number on his leg.

Chris Caddle rang me to pass on his condolences last night, and I ended up roaring at him and asking him why the hell his crowd won't protect their own people any more? Maybe we should do it ourselves? But he just told me to get some sleep and we'd talk about it later in the week.

Chris went through this himself not three months ago and thankfully knows not to take me on. But he's right. I'm too angry.

Wednesday, May 26

Even Fr Noel couldn't offer anything. "Burying a young person is always terrible," he said, "because what we're really doing is burying our future. And burying Frank seems worse again, because we all know Frank had one glorious future."

I stood by the graveside with Frank's family, taking condolences like a total fraud. The whole parish knows he was shot because of me. Though they were far too kind to say so. Most of them anyway.

"He really admired you," said Mary Naughton as she gave me a hug. "I told him he was wasting his time. But he said you were fundamentally honest. The worst thing about all of this is that Frank was committed to what he was doing – he really thought politics could make things better. He hadn't an ounce of cynicism in him. You, you're only in it because you're too shallow to do anything else. If I'm going to be honest, I'm sorry they didn't wait for you."

Afterwards in the Jack Kennedy, Tommy Bowtie had his turn. "Mary's right," he said. "You think you're too good for this business. You look down your nose at it. You won't commit to an argument, you won't commit to principles, and you won't commit to a party.

"And it's no coincidence that you won't commit to a woman either. You're very charming, Shay, but you're totally superficial. Truth is, the real reason you can't hold down a girl is that as soon as they go looking for any hidden depths, they run out of water..."

Shallow, arrogant, cynical. They're right, of course.

Good job I'm a total coward as well, or I'd have gone home and shot myself.

Friday, May 28

Reading the Loyalist Action Group's website is like reading a toilet wall. The topics are always the lowest common denominator – and they're both written by lowlifes and perverts.

Stan Stevenson rang me last night to tell me that the LAG had posted a claim of responsibility for Frank's killing on the site. And he warned me that they were making extremely nasty allegations about me – some of which, he said, were likely to appear in some tabloids over the weekend.

To be honest, I didn't want to give the LAG the satisfaction of reading their hate mail, but given that I'm bound to be questioned about it within the very near future, I logged on. Christ it was grim.

A user calling himself "The Colonel" had written a "communiqué" under their "Recent Successes" column in which he admitted the LAG had "assassinated Shay Gallagher's eyes and ears, Francis McNickell". The stupid bastards couldn't even spell his name.

"McNickell," wrote the Colonel, "paid the ultimate penalty for his association with Shay Gallagher.

"Ten years ago, Sue McEwan, daughter of an eminent Protestant family and now a politician serving Ulster, was raped and impregnated by a gang of Fenian hoods. The LAG have in our possession, files given to us by the police that prove Gallagher was involved. Our South Antrim battalion have also reported that he raped her a second time in a Belfast hotel earlier this year.

"Gallagher is a known Provo supporter who has publicly and wrongly named innocent Protestants as LAG operatives, so putting their lives in terrible danger. We believe that Gallagher used McNickell, a well-known GAA player, to gather information on local Protestants, which he would then pass on to his friends in the IRA.

"So today, we are issuing this warning to all friends of Shay Gallagher: disown him, or you also will be a target. Likewise, our message to Mr Gallagher is simple – we only have to be lucky once, you have to be lucky all the time. Ha! Ha!"

Goebbels would have been proud of these guys – 50 percent lies and 50 percent scaremongering, with just enough fact thrown in to ensure some of the shit sticks.

The PSNI rang while I was still logged onto the site to let me know they had already been contacted by two journalists asking about the rape claims. In fairness to the cops, they immediately blew the suggestions out of the water. Pity, in a way – I'd have loved some of the scumbags to print it, so I could have Tommy Bowtie sue their arses off.

Monday, May 31

Sue Mack had sent flowers to the funeral, but decided not to appear. As it was, most of the Sunday cheapsheets yesterday linked Frank's death to our friendship – or as one rag put it: REPUBLICAN PIN-UP BOY GALLAGHER'S TORRID HISTORY WITH LOYALIST VAMP SUE MCEWAN. True to form, all of them suggested Frank had Provo connections – with one of them describing him as a former IRA intelligence officer.

Hell will never be full as long as there are journalists in the world.

I think it's time to ring Sue and have a chat about the elephant in our living room. Though I'll give it a day or two to let the hysteria die down a bit first.

●●●●●●●

I'd rung Sue myself and begged her not to appear at the funeral. If she'd turned up, everything would have been about her and Shay. Frank's family would have been a sideshow. Every front page would have carried the picture of Shay and Sue together at the graveside with some typical lowbrow headline like: SHOT FOR OUR LOVE. Shay's right — there should be a special circle of hell set aside for the press.

Sue really wanted to come though — she'd got to know Frank well over the past couple of months. He'd long stopped ringing her on pretexts — they both knew he was keeping the door open for Shay. And it gave Sue a chance to find out how her own Great White Hope was behaving. Not that Frank would have given away too much, mind. Just enough to keep her interested.

I'm glad Mary Naughton had a rattle at Shay at the cemetery. I don't feel as bad now about the going-over I gave him afterwards in the pub. Shay spent too many years as a teacher talking down to people. You need to pull him up now and again.

JUNE 2004

There was a general feeling that Frank's death might be the end of things, but I wasn't convinced. I figured the LAG would be smart enough to lay low for a few weeks — maybe even a couple of months. But it had gone too far for them to forget about Shay; he was an itch that they would always have to scratch.

Obviously there was no telling Shay that. It's not that he doesn't hear, more that it doesn't register. He has a very academic approach to the real world and had managed to convince himself that God was giving him immunity. But regardless, he'd no business running back to Sue. It was a straight two-fingers into their faces.

Emile's disc had revealed that Stovell was more unhinged than we thought. And the really good news was that he was fixated with Sue. So at a time when Shay should have been laying low as a Larne Catholic, he was out front and centre, playing kissy-face with the pyscho's imaginary girlfriend.

•••••••

Thursday, June 3

The journey from Derry to Omagh is only 35 miles, but the GTI's been acting up, so I left myself an hour. Realistically, you're as well to give yourself an hour at the best of times, anyway. Gregory opened a new ring road at Newtownstewart when he was DRD minister, prompting the tongue-in-cheek headline: DUP MAN MAKES DUBLIN ROAD SHORTER. But the traffic flow is far too heavy for a road its size, so even the bypass makes little odds.

Tommy Bowtie did his best to stop me going. But if you lived all your life by what lawyers tell you, you'd never get up in the morning.

"You simply cannot see her again," he said. "It's a direct challenge to them. They will have to kill you. It will be their life's mission. Stovell and Townslow are obsessed with Sue – she's their equivalent of the Virgin Mary, and you are the devil incarnate trying to corrupt her."

"Does it say all this on your disc?" I snapped.

"Look, Shay," he pleaded, "it says this and a whole lot worse. These guys are evil, evil, evil. They killed Stumpy, Aileen, Frank and a whole graveyard full of others over the last ten years. And now they want you.

"Your best bet is to take off for about a month's holiday. Stay out of sight. Otherwise, I guarantee I'm going to wind up carrying another coffin before the end of this year."

I know Tommy meant well, but lawyers are the most pessimistic people in the world. The glass is always half-cracked.

Despite the portents of doom, I got to Omagh safely and in good time to meet Sue at the Indian restaurant on Campsie Road. She was already there, in a secluded corner booth, drinking a Cobra beer. She looked, not to put too fine a point on it, like hell. Give credit to her, she was trying – and had decked herself out in a Ralph Lauren suit with immaculate patent leather Italian pumps. But her skin was white and pasty, her green eyes were dull, and her fiery red hair was matted and seemed to have lost its sheen.

"I haven't slept since they killed him," she explained. "He was a great guy. Kept tabs on you for me. Always told me I'd nothing to worry about, because I was the only girl who ever made you sing in the mornings – and the only one who ever made you punch a hole in your office wall.

"But for all that, he never told me anything that was going to get you into bother. Always batted for you. Let's face it, he died batting for you. The problem is, and we've both read the website, while he may have died for you – I'm the reason they shot him. I'm their justification."

"I've been down the same road myself, Sue," I told her, "it doesn't go anywhere."

"Not what I'm talking about, Shay," she interrupted, fiercely. "I should have told you this before, but I've known Rex Stovell a long time. I haven't spoken to him in almost a decade. I mean, why would I, he's the most twisted and evil little man in all of Ulster. He used to hang around the fringes of the Unionist Society at Coleraine and I met him once or twice – and now he's got this screwed up idea that he's my protector.

"Shortly after I struck up with you, the police warned me Stovell was going to try something. But you knew you were on his list anyway, because of the big row in the council. And we were never that serious, so I didn't think to say anything."

Funny, it doesn't surprise me that Sue would know a thug like Stovell. She could almost be a nationalist sometimes, the way she thumbs her nose at authority – probably a reaction to her daddy being a judge and all.

"Don't blame yourself over Frank, Sue," I said and took her hand. "You're right – we knew the boys were coming for me. We even knew they were coming that weekend. And by all accounts, they'll try again.

"Tommy Bowtie's jumping up and down because I came here this afternoon. He says if I'm seen with you again, they'll do me before the day's out."

"So what do you think?"

"My only worry," I said, "is if they came for me and got you instead."

"Very noble of you," said Sue quietly. "But if they ever do come for you, Shay, I'll be standing in front of you."

There's no answer to that. So I just cupped her two hands in mine and nodded thanks.

"So are you asking me out, like officially, now?" piped up Sue suddenly, a spark returning to her eyes.

"Well, why not?" I grinned. "I've never seen you looking worse – puffy face, lousy hair and tikka masala all over your teeth. There's not much left for me to be scared of."

"That's good," laughed Sue, "because I want you to drive out to Greencastle with me now and explain to Danielle why I've cut off all her cable channels…"

Monday, June 7

Sue and I released a joint press statement this morning, announcing the establishment of the Francis McNicholl Memorial

Scholarship. We're each chipping in £500 a year, which will go to the most promising politics student at Queen's, where Frank studied. The McNicholl family are putting up another £500, and Mary Naughton has persuaded the SDLP to stick in a grand.

Tommy Bowtie is knocking back Valium by the bottle. He says I might as well have walked into Rex Stovell's front room and shat on his sofa.

Friday, June 11

I kept my office open during most of polling yesterday, which wasn't the smartest idea I ever had, as people kept coming in to ask me which way to vote. And it becomes a lot more complicated when you realise that that all of the parties are sending up a spy or two to find out which way the Gallagher wind is blowing.

Frank would have known how to handle them. I kicked for touch and advised them to go with their conscience.

Sue was facing a similar predicament across in Tyrone. Her talks with the UUP collapsed when somebody told her it would be nice to have a good-looking face on the front bench – now that Arlene and Norah are gone. And her father would turn in his grave if she'd anything to do with the working-class oiks in the DUP.

Both of us ended up voting for Gilliland – me on the grounds that he's from Derry, Sue because he's a bit of a babe. Didn't matter a damn though, as it was always going to be Bairbre and the two Jims.

The people have spoken… Baaaa.

Monday, June 14

Stuck my head round the door of the count at the Waterfront this morning, but only to return Sue's brochures to her. "Real couples go on holiday together," she told me, when we hooked up for tea at the Everglades yesterday.

"Count me in, so," I replied, "but only if Danielle can come along too."

"You're very sweet," said Sue with a warm smile that boded well for later that night. "As if you'd any choice, anyway…"

Sue was up at the count to see how the unionist vote was splitting in the East Tyrone boxes, as it'll certainly influence her stance on the Agreement for the next year or two. Because there's no constituency-by-constituency breakdown in the Euro poll, tallymen from all over the Six Counties were attempting to do it on the hoof. It's a pretty inexact science though.

Back in the real world, Sue and I agreed on Italy for the last week of June and the first week in July.

We had talked about the Free State as we're both big fans of the outright ban on smoking. But the South has become fierce dear, maybe the most expensive place in Europe. And besides, we've both been invited to summer schools in Donegal in August, all expenses paid.

Sue then suggested Croatia, but I objected on the grounds that she'd only want to fill her suitcase full of guns for the UDA. I in turn mooted Bogotá on the basis that they like Irish people so much, they give them free bed and board. Sure, even the Colombia Three are staying on. But Sue said that while she'd love to, both she and Danielle have got totally valid passports. And besides, the real reason the three muchachos won't come home is that they've heard they'll have to sit on a plane with Caitriona Ruane for 14 hours.

So Italy it is. The little town of Montefiascone, just up the hill from Lake Bolsena. I read up about it and discovered that all the popes used to holiday there, before they got Castel Gandolfo. Compromised, and told Sue it was Martin Luther's summer retreat.

Wednesday, June 16

Didn't get home to Derry until 1.00am this morning, after the GTI broke down again on the Foreglen. A three-year-old Volkswagen with only 50,000 miles on the clock. There should be a law.

The entire evening had been spent sorting out the thousand or so condolence cards that had poured into the office, which I then left up to the McNicholls in two big binbags. The cards came from right across the political spectrum and included messages from both premiers.

Dexter Hart – who'd bought Frank drink all night at the Mayor's Ball to apologise for their clash at the Brandywell – wrote me a note expressing his deep sorrow at the loss of such a talented protégé and "committed" sportsman. And he also enclosed a copy of a letter he'd dispatched to the Press Complaints Commission accusing several local papers of defiling Frank's good name with their "baseless" accusations. Dexter, who's really far too decent to be in politics, knows it'll carry a lot more weight coming from him.

Tony Blunt also sent a sympathy card though, personally, I feel the hypocrite is just keeping his ducks in a row for whenever he's found out. Took his card up to the McNicholls, regardless. But somewhat surprisingly, they told me they'd got one from the DUP man already.

Needless to say, there's been the predictable smattering of death threats for my good self among the envelopes. One Mass card, indeed, had my name on it and contained a .303 bullet. The card was signed 'SAT', which Tommy Bowtie tells me is a cute little nom de guerre 'S'tovell and 'T'ownslow sometimes use for their joint operations. The cops were only able to hold them for 24 hours after Frank's killing, as a former Special Branch officer had passed them in a Coleraine carpark at the exact time of the shooting. Lucky for them, or what?

Friday, June 18
Danny Moorhead, my mechanic, tells me there's a very simple reason that the GTI's been playing up – it's been clocked.

I bought it from Barney McBain less than a year ago, after he convinced me it was the best motor on his forecourt. He'd just imported it from England, it was only two years old and it had only 30,000 miles on the dash. And the engine, I was told, was clean as a bedtime story.

"I can tell you for certain," insisted Danny, "that someone's docked at least 70,000 miles from the mileometer. If you look closely at the chassis beside the timing belt, you'll see a little sticker saying the timing belt was replaced when the car was only a year old. Now you'll only ever do that if there's at least 50,000 miles on the clock. And you can be guaranteed the car did another 50,000 in her second year, as the timing belt that's in her now was almost new when you bought her.

"Your problem is, when you go back to McBain, he'll swear to you he knows nothing about it. He'll say it was clocked when it was across the water. But take it from me; he's a lying bastard.

"There's a guy who travels round the garages here with a laptop computer he can plug into a car's computer memory. For £80, cash, he'll rewrite your mileage to whatever you want. And he's never out of McBain's. They call him 'Dock-It' Doherty. He used to be a teacher like you, but he retired to do this, because it pays a lot better. He even advertises in the paper under 'Dashboard repairs'."

Danny reckons that about a quarter of the cars and half the vans on the road here are clocked. There's also a whole squad of DLA drivers, who aren't allowed to do more than 5,000 miles a year, but are taxiing on the side, and then knocking off the miles again.

"You should report McBain to the police," he said. "If you put it in pounds, shillings and pence, he conned you out of about £2,000. He's committing wholesale fraud – pure and simple.

"Use my name, and tell the cops if they want to talk to me, I have personally seen another 20 – no, another <u>50</u> – cars McBain has sold that were clocked."

Easier said than done. As a loyal son of Ulster, Danny would have no qualms about sinking McBain to the Gendarmes. But I, as a proud Irish citizen, am still reluctant to shop a fellow countryman to the organs of the Northern state.

Truth is, I'm not wild about any colour of cops anyway. As Uncle Shay used to say, a policeman will only ever use a situation to <u>his</u> advantage – never to yours. Though I suppose that's true of everybody. But generally, by the time you're thinking about calling the police, you've already lost and are only looking for a tooth for your tooth.

There's a further difficulty in this case in that I can't sort it out locally, as McBain is a cousin of Chris Caddle. And while Chris would never condone Barney's crookery, he's not going to vote against him at a private tribunal either.

I rang Sue Mack for advice, though to be honest, I wasn't expecting much. Planters tend to have a very black-and-white view of criminality and how to deal with it, whereas we natives can hardly see through the grey.

Sue, however, cut right through the fog.

"Sell me the car," she said simply. "Or at least, give me the log book, and I'll take it back to McBain and tell him I've bought it. I'll assure him I have proof it's been clocked and that I've been ripped off. I'll tell him my mechanic will testify that Dock-It Doherty did the work for him, and that unless he gives me two grand out of his till, I'll close him down.

"If the worst comes to the worst, I've no hang-ups about setting the police on him. But we'll not have to."

So I left the logbook down to Sue at teatime. But when I got home to Derry and dropped into the Delacroix for a pint with Tommy Bowtie, he started giving me dog's abuse.

"You should have turned him in right away," he said. "You were ready to let a thief steal two grand off you because the Shinners haven't given you the go-ahead to call in the police. You're softer than you look.

"Everyone knows they have to sign up to policing – even their own hardliners. The Shinners are starting to grow quite a handsome middle-class vote. And the smart republicans know they'll not keep them unless they give them a standalone police service that'll protect them – and their property – from the great unwashed.

"Can't come soon enough for my money."

Tommy Bowtie backing the police? Jesus, now there's a turnaround. Next thing, the Drumcree Orangemen will be admitting the Garvaghy Road residents have a point.

Tuesday, June 22

Sue called to say that she's spoken to Barney McBain and got my three grand back.

"But he only owed me two," I told her.

"So he did," she replied. "But I'm flat broke and needed some spending money for the holiday."

Wednesday, June 23

Stan Stevenson from the Standard rang yesterday – "just for a chat" – and casually mentioned that he'd heard Tony Blunt was negotiating with the Loyalist Action Group to try and bring about a ceasefire.

I told Stan it was news to me, and he agreed there was probably nothing in it. But the front-page story in today's paper – which incidentally was written by one Stanley Stevenson – would beg to differ:

BLUNT IN TALKS TO LIFT LAG THREAT
By Stan Stevenson

Dunavady DUP alderman Tony Blunt has been involved in secret dialogue with loyalists to get them to lift their death threat on independent MLA Shay Gallagher, it was disclosed last night.

Mr Blunt has refused to comment on the two meetings, which are understood to have taken place at The King's Head Hotel in Drumbridge. But the LAG revealed to this paper yesterday that the DUP man met them last week to discuss a permanent ceasefire.

A spokesperson for the LAG, who identified himself only as 'The Colonel', commented: "Alderman Blunt has asked us to come back to him with our conditions for calling a permanent ceasefire, and for removing our fatwah from the leading republican Shay Gallagher. In the interests of lowering the political temperature in the run-up to the marching season, we have agreed to consider his request.

"We will be engaging in further talks with unionist political leaders over the next month, and during this time, we have agreed to uphold a short-term truce. Though at all times, we reserve the right to engage in defensive action."

The PSNI declared last night that the talks would not inhibit their hunt for the killers of Francis McNicholl.

"The LAG are very much mistaken if they think they can murder innocent people in cold blood one minute and then try and hide behind political cover," Superintendent Audrey Grafton told the Standard.

"This group of gangsters have been responsible for three brutal murders in North Derry in the past eight months. It would be dishonouring the memory of their victims to give them a 'Get out of jail free' card for a promise of future good behaviour."

The UUP's Dexter Hart was also sceptical about the short-term truce.

"If Shay Gallagher can sleep a little sounder in his bed tonight, then Tony Blunt's efforts have to be welcomed," he said.

"But the LAG's move comes far too late for John O'Rourke, Aileen Bates and my own friend Frank McNicholl. And I for one will insist that there is absolutely no political interference to prevent the police bringing those who have been involved in recent violence to justice."

Sinn Féin and the SDLP have both given a guarded welcome to the LAG statement. Shay Gallagher, meanwhile, told the Standard he was unaware of the talks.

Thursday, June 24

Sue came up from Greencastle last night for Frank's Month's Mind. Fr Noel used part of his sermon to dismiss the LAG's truce as "craven opportunism" and then presented Stan Stevenson with a typed copy, in case he missed the point.

Sue hadn't met Mary Naughton since their debacle at the Brandywell, but I needn't have worried. As soon as the pair saw one another, they did that instant-forgiveness thing that women are a whole lot better at than men, and gave each other a hug. "Be good to Shay," Mary told Sue. "Life's too short."

Then first thing this morning, Tony Blunt rang to apologise for coming off like a big star in the paper and getting mileage out of my difficulties. He insisted that he'd nothing to do with leaking the story to the paper. And I have to say, he sounded almost convincing.

"I'm sorry, Shay," he said. "The whole thing was a waste of time. They're just window-dressing. When I pressed one of them – off the record, Stovell – about what they'd need to call off their campaign for good, he said: 'Well, for a start, there'll be no ceasefire as long as Shay Gallagher's defiling our women.'"

"So are you telling me to give up Sue for the sake of the peace?" I asked Blunt.

"No way," he said. "I'd never bow to bullies like them. If I were you, I'd marry Sue in the morning. And you'd have my best wishes too – she might knock a bit of sense into you."

●●●●●●●

Stovell had made a reel of Blunt, and Blunt knew it. I rang him myself afterwards to ask him what in Christ's name he was playing at, and he assured me "on Carson's grave" that the LAG hoodlums had set him up. They'd worked out they were backing themselves into a corner and were looking for political cover. So they contacted Blunt with the promise of a "cessation". The DUP man saw the headline and went along to the meeting, but he wasn't in the door five minutes before he realised they were only putting on a show. And as soon as he figured out he was being used, he walked out.

In fairness to Blunt, he thought he might have done some good. But the whole episode really embarrassed him. It left him angry as hell, in fact. And Tony Blunt is not a man that you'd want to have mad at you.

On the plus side, we did well to shunt Shay off to Italy for a couple of weeks. He'd his heart set on a fortnight in the west of Ireland, but we got Sue to talk him round by telling him it was far too dear. Of course, what she didn't say was that the LAG goons were much less likely to follow Shay through an airport with loaded weapons.

JULY 2004

The great thing about being a prophet of doom in this country is that most of the time you get to be proved right. Not that I take much pride in it though — it's too easy.

Unlike me, however, Shay is one of those guys who can't believe that the world could ever conspire against him. And he's happy to spend his days staring into the volcano, wondering why the pretty bubbles are getting bigger. The upside of this, however, is that when the lava starts pelting down on his head, it's over before he knows it — and he hasn't lost half his life worrying about it.

•••••••

Sunday, July 11

I'd never travelled abroad with a woman before. It's very different from holidaying with men in that you don't get to spend all day, everyday, drinking and chasing women. But I can't deny it, it was terrific. We barely stopped laughing for two full weeks.

Sue was a revelation. As soon as she got out of the North, all the angst lifted and we were two (well, three) normal – and very happy – human beings. I still can't figure out how it worked so well, because she failed all the tests. She never shut her mouth from morning to night, never once brought me breakfast-in-bed, stole all my T-shirts and made me hold hands in public restaurants. In the good old days, she would have ended up owing me gold stars.

Danielle, likewise, had a great time and charmed all the natives by carrying an Italian phrase book everywhere to order her gelato, biscotti and arancia. The three of us spent most of the afternoons on Lake Bolsena, boating, swimming and catching shoals of little catfish, who proved to be very stupid animals indeed. One person swims behind them and then chases them towards their buddy holding the net. As Sue said, it's as easy as rounding up Fenians in a late-night riot.

Montefiascone town is famous for its white wine, though I wasn't entirely convinced. In the Middle Ages, a German bishop who was holidaying in Italy sent a scout ahead of him to all the local towns to sample the wine. If it was any good, the scout was to write 'Est' ('It is') on the main entrance to the town, but apparently he was so taken by Montefiascone's drink that he painted 'Est! Est!! Est!!!' on the gate. Personally, I wouldn't use it to strip the engine of a dodgy GTI.

It wasn't possible, however, to escape politics entirely, and on our last night we wound up having dinner with two MPs from Berlusconi's Forza Italia party. Like government parties everywhere, they'd taken a bit of a pasting at the Euro polls, but they were upbeat that their centre-right coalition would recover from the stagger.

Unusually for Italians, they were particularly knowledgeable about the North, and their long-term prognosis was not good at all.

"No-one cares about you," said Gianfranco, who did a masters at Cambridge and has visited the Six Counties twice. "The British want rid of you – you're too much of a drain, and the Irish will never adopt you for the same reason. Even the EU looks on you like a big leech. But you'd need to be damn careful now with ten new countries all looking to drink from the well.

"Over here, we regard the Northern Irish as the most inward-looking people in Europe. September 11 and the Iraq War passed you by, because you don't give a damn about anything outside your own little patch of dirt. Every other country in Europe is working to improve itself, but you lot are like a bad Punch and Judy show.

"And it's not as if you've anything really to contribute to Europe. Look around you at Italy, France, Germany, Spain, Portugal – and even Britain. They all have strong economies, productive industrial sectors, highly developed tourist sectors, and they're all rich in art, history and literature.

"What have you? A whiskey distillery, a bunch of strange-looking rocks pointing towards Scotland, and endless lines of monuments to dead people."

And there was little comfort either from Francesca, who holds a seat in north Lazio.

"All your entrepreneurial spirit and ambition has been choked out of you," she said. "You're so bent on fighting with one another that you miss every chance to help yourselves. You're like the economics professor who refuses to pick up the 50-euro note lying on the ground – because it couldn't really be a 50-euro note, or someone else would have picked it up already."

It was a fairly sober end to an otherwise carefree trip. And it doesn't make it any easier to argue your corner when you arrive back to Aldergrove to see all the headlines predicting mayhem after tomorrow's marches.

We are Millwall, We are Millwall, No-one likes us, We don't care.

Wednesday, July 14

The entirety of the BBC and UTV news yesterday was devoted to Monday night's post-march rioting. I switched over to RTE at teatime and noticed that the trouble didn't even make the third headline. Gianfranco is right, the South don't want to know – why the hell would they?

Friday, July 16

Sue called last night to give me a hard time about how the Morris Report has accepted that the Gardaí planted their own bombs and then blamed the IRA. Indeed, her spiel on Free State corruption was going rightly until I reminded her that the last Northern police force was so rotten, they had to close it down.

But her tail was up, and there was no stopping her. "You couldn't trust a Garda with a well-dressed corpse, as my late father always said," she sniffed.

She wasn't getting away with that. "Do you know that Morris actually offered to hold a similar inquiry into the Special Branch up here?" I asked her.

"I suppose you're going to claim it was stopped by political interference," she replied.

"No," I told her. "They were afraid the world would run out of paper."

It's Danielle's tenth birthday this weekend so we're off to Dublin for a spree in the morning – shopping, cinema, beauty-pampering and a tour of the Guinness brewery. (We were allowed one treat each.)

Sue put Danielle on the phone, while she went off to deal with a client at the door. And seizing her chance, Danielle demanded to know if I would buy her a mobile phone for a present.

"It'd be great security for me," she pleaded in a voice that was just a little too sweet. "And it would put Mommy's mind at rest when I'm out of the house."

"They fry your brain, Danielle," I replied. "And anyway, who'd pay for your line rental and all your calls?"

"You or Mommy could, Shay," she said. "And it would be very useful to keep the contact up the next time you're in the doghouse."

"You really are a devious little witch," I chuckled, "but no. No way. Sue would tie me up and beat me to death. And not in a fun way either."

"Tell you what, so," continued Danielle, changing pace, "if you get me one, I'll tell Nana that I'm sleeping in the same room with Mommy in Dublin this weekend. Just like I told her I always shared a double room with Mommy in Italy."

"That's out and out blackmail," I protested. "If you were five years older, you'd go to jail."

"Mommy doesn't even have to know about it," said Danielle, without missing a beat. "And if you get me the Nokia 3200, I'll not tell her that you threw that silk tie she bought you in the bin at the airport. Let's face it, Shay, you're wide open."

"I'm shocked – totally shocked," I said, trying not to laugh. "What do you think your mother would say if she heard you talking like that?"

"Why don't I tell her myself, Shay?" interrupted Sue suddenly with a nasty giggle. "Sorry, Danielle, but Mommy's been listening in on the other extension..." And with that, there was a brief squeal, and the line went dead.

Nice try, Dee, but when you're dealing with pros, you gotta suit up for the game.

Now all I have to do is find another orange-and-yellow striped Versace tie before tomorrow morning.

Monday, July 19
FUCK. FUCK. FUCK. This can't be happening. We're just back from Dublin.

Sue rang in complete hysterics ten minutes ago. Two men with scarves over their faces are after bursting into her mother's house, tying up Old Ma and bundling Danielle into a van.

I called the cops and got patched through to Audrey Grafton. She asked me to hold fire at the flat until she could get a jeep to escort my car down to Greencastle.

Maybe if I keep writing in my diary it will all go away.

Wednesday, July 21
Called home to Derry for a change of clothes and to get a brief respite from the hateful waiting and doing nothing. Sue is veering between being a terrified mother who just wants her baby back, and the tough-ass politician who knows it would be suicide for the gang to harm her daughter.

Not once, however, has she blamed me. Not once. The papers are a lot less kind and are full of unhelpful suggestions as to why it's all my fault – except maybe the Standard, which plays it straight down the middle:

KILLER GANG BEHIND DANIELLE SNATCH
By Stan Stevenson

Police were last night refusing to confirm or deny claims that the Loyalist Action Group abducted Danielle McEwan, daughter of the independent unionist MLA Sue McEwan, on Monday night.

Their comments follow yesterday's telephone call from the suspected kidnappers to Dunavady DUP councillor Tony Blunt, in which they outlined a number of conditions for the nine-year-old's safe release.

Mr Blunt has refused to make public the demands, or to comment on the kidnapping, other than to say he believed that the LAG were involved.

"This is far too important to get wrong," he told the Standard. "A little Protestant girl's life is at stake."

Shay Gallagher MLA, who is a close personal friend of the McEwan family, has spent the past two days at their Tyrone farm. The North Derry assemblyman has himself previously been the subject of numerous LAG death threats, and his chief advisor, Francis McNicholl, was shot dead by the murder gang just two months ago.

The LAG also warned in May that all associates of Mr Gallagher should either disown him or consider themselves "legitimate targets". And there is now growing concern that they are making good their threat.

Broadcast

In a televised address to the kidnappers broadcast last night, a grief-stricken Sue McEwan pleaded for the immediate return of her child.

"Is your hatred so deep that you would harm your own kind because her mother has Catholic friends?" said Ms McEwan.

Shay Gallagher said both he and the McEwan family would do "whatever it takes" to get Danielle back safely. "We'll listen to all the demands and consider all the options," he said.

The PSNI, meanwhile, have launched a full-scale search operation in the Magilligan area where the gang are thought to have a stronghold.

And while the police are refusing to say for certain if LAG members are involved, they have announced that they would like to speak to leading loyalists Rex Stovell and Wilbur Townslow in connection with the kidnapping. The two men were named by Dunavady councillors earlier this year as the LAG killers of Sinn Féin Assembly candidate John 'Stumpy' O'Rourke.

Superintendent Audrey Grafton said: "These men are highly dangerous. They have been suspects in a number of murders. Don't approach them. Call us directly."

Sinn Féin, meanwhile, have appealed for people in the area, who may have information about the killing, but are reluctant to talk to the police, to get in touch with them.

Meanwhile, Danielle McEwan's 62-year-old grandmother Agnes is recovering in hospital after her wrist was broken during the abduction.

During the struggle, the battling granny smashed a heavy crystal vase over the head of one of the gang members. Blood discovered at the scene suggests that the kidnapper may have suffered a substantial gash.

Stan Stevenson's report is all the better, given that he knows a whole lot more than he's letting on, including the fact that the LAG gang intend to swap Danielle for me. I suspected that's what it was about the minute I got Sue's call on Monday – and Tony Blunt confirmed it when he called down to see me in Greencastle yesterday morning.

When Sue came in, Blunt, quite graciously, told her that the gang's main demand was the release of six prisoners from Maghaberry jail. It was a barefaced lie, but it sure as hell beats 'Who would you rather get shot, Miss McEwan – your boyfriend or your daughter?'

I spoke to Blunt on the phone again yesterday afternoon when we agreed to put Stan and Fr Noel in the loop. Both sides want two independent witnesses present – one from each 'community' – when we perform the switch.

Saturday, July 24

Got the word from Blunt. It's on for tonight. He and I, along with Stan and Fr Noel, have to go to the Stag's Head Bar in Dunavady for nine o'clock and wait for a call.

I told Sue I had to return to Derry for the night to visit Fr. Noel's brother, who's been moved into the hospice. Fr Noel himself even rang me at Sue's house to set up the decoy.

Agnes got out of hospital yesterday so she'll be able to keep Sue company for the night. The old dear has been so nice to me since she came home, it's unnerving. She's made it very clear she doesn't hold me responsible for what's happened to Danielle. In fact, she told me I was all that was standing between Sue and the Clinic. Sue's still wearing her brave face, but she gets up during the night and goes down to the living room to cry when she thinks I'm asleep.

Agnes was disappointed when I said I had to go back to Derry for the night. But she's not buying the hospice visit one bit. As I left the house, she caught me with one sharp eye and said, "For God's sake be very careful, son. Sue needs you back as well."

I'm not used to being appreciated like this. Excuse me a minute, Mrs McEwan, but have you forgotten I'm a Fenian?

Tuesday, July 27
Released from Dunavady Police Station at eight o'clock last night. I might finally have my life back.

PSNI STATEMENT

Witness name: *Seamus Patrick (Shay) Gallagher MLA*

Address: *Marina Apartments, Strand Road, Derry*

DoB: *October 15, 1970*

Interview date/time: *July 26, 6.00pm*

Persons present: *Audrey Grafton (Supt. PSNI), Douglas McDonald (DCI PSNI), Thomas McGinlay (Solicitor)*

I had been instructed to go the Stag's Head in Dunavady town, along with Fr Noel Giddens, Stanley Stevenson and Tony Blunt, and wait for a call. At about 9.30pm, the phone rang and the barmaid called for me. When I lifted the receiver, a male voice asked me if I knew where Downhill Castle was, and when I said I did, he instructed the four of us to travel there in my car. He knew it was a GTI. He said that the car would be under surveillance the whole way from Dunavady to make sure no-one was following us. When we got to the estate, we were to park the car at the Lion Gate and walk to the Mussenden Temple about half a mile away, right up by the cliff. Hands on our heads the whole way.

There's a small fence around the temple, and a gate about 30 yards from the front steps. Fr Noel, Stan and Tony were to wait at that gate, while I went into the temple. The caller said that as soon as I was in the door, they would release Danielle and the other three could take her home. He said that they would then question me in relation to "terrorist crime" and let me go within 24 hours.

The journey to the castle took about 30 minutes. I drove. Fr Noel recited a decade of the rosary in the car. Even Stan Stevenson joined in. Then, we all remained silent while Tony Blunt said a prayer of his own. I checked the mirror about a thousand times in case the police were following me. I was very scared the whole thing would go wrong.

As we passed through Downhill village, I thought I heard some thunderclaps nearby. Tony said he had heard on the wireless before going out that there could be lightning along the north coast.

It was still daylight when I parked the GTI at the main entrance of the estate. We had all been at the castle before, so we headed straight up the hill towards the temple. All of us had our hands on our heads as instructed – and nobody spoke a word.

As we approached the temple, I could see a dim light shining out the window. Very dim. Nothing that you would see from Lough Foyle below.

We reached the fence around the temple, and I waited for a slow count of 60 for any sign of movement. But nothing seemed to be stirring at all. So I straddled the gate, and headed for the steps. I looked back briefly and saw Fr Noel bless me.

I got to the door of the temple and twisted the handle slowly. I heard soft crying inside and knew immediately it was Danielle. So I pushed the door open and walked inside.

The circular room was lit by a small gaslight, and Danielle was lying sobbing under a tall lattice window just opposite the entrance. She looked up and without saying a word, pointed out the window to the cliff ledge on the right. There, the bodies of three men were lying, all motionless. I could make out pools of blood beside the bodies. There was still enough daylight outside for me to recognise two of the men as Rex Stovell and Wilbur Townslow – I'd been shown their pictures on a police montage after Frank McNicholl was murdered. The third man, who was about a foot-and-a-half taller than the other pair, I had never seen before.

I rushed outside to see if there was anything I could do for the men, but they all appeared to be dead. So I lifted Danielle up off the floor and left the temple.

As soon as I got her out, I shouted to the others to come quickly. I stayed at the gate with Danielle to ring Sue McEwan, Danielle's mother, while Fr Noel gave the three men the last rites. Tony Blunt and Stan Stevenson are both trained in first aid, and they checked out the bodies for signs of life. But it was too late.

As soon as Danielle had finished talking to her mother, I called the police, who arrived very shortly afterwards.

Audrey Grafton told me my statement tallied almost word for word with Tony Blunt's, Fr Noel's and Stan's. So detailed and so neat. We'd even explained everybody's fingerprints on the bodies. And she didn't believe a word of it.

On Sunday, they had done powder tests on my hands for firearms, which had come back negative. So had the other three's. But Audrey was still threatening to charge all of us with conspiracy to murder. "I won't tolerate vigilantism on my patch," she said. "Even people like Stovell and Townslow deserve due process."

Tommy Bowtie then asked her would she be prepared to confirm, on the record, that two of the dead men were Special Branch agents, as she'd suggested at the DPP meeting earlier this year after Aileen Bates was killed. If the police had applied due process back then, he pointed out, these guys would have been in jail before they got the chance to kill Frank McNicholl and kidnap Danielle.

Audrey lowered her eyes. She was bluffing and we all knew it. Besides, she'd some cleaning up of her own to do.

"One thing," she said, before she let me out of the interview room. "You were mistaken about the number of casualties outside the temple. There were only two – Stovell and Townslow. As you can imagine, we did a thorough search of the area and I would emphasise that no other body was found.

"You were under great stress at the time and, for whatever reason – panic maybe – you now misremember what you saw there. Furthermore, I would strongly advise you against suggesting to the press that anyone else was present at the temple. The media have quite enough to occupy their minds with Danielle arriving home and the deaths of Stovell and Townslow, without going off on a wild goose chase for another body."

Tommy Bowtie nodded over at me to take the hint. They've obviously been warned to hush up the fact that Emile was there.

The police suggested that I amend my statement later in the week, after I've rested up.

Wednesday, July 28

The neighbours threw a homecoming party for Danielle in Greencastle yesterday afternoon – right about the same time they were burying the two LAG vermin back in north Derry.

She seems to have bounced back well, though Sue is refusing to let her talk to the police, as she's already suffered enough trauma. There'll be a row over this later, but Tommy Bowtie has assured us the cops will never get past him.

We've established that the abductors treated Danielle very well; one of them even called her "princess". Apparently they fed her on a diet of chips and coke after she told them she was "lactose intolerant". (Dee was a Health Channel addict before Mommy cut off the Cable.) She must have spent the entire week on a sugar high.

In the middle of the party, Stan Stevenson landed down with a copy of the Standard for my edification. His report was a work of art:

DANIELLE FREED BY
'BLACK OPS' UNIT – EXCLUSIVE
By Stan Stevenson

Security sources last night confirmed that the Special Air Service (SAS) were behind last week's rescue of Danielle McEwan and the shooting dead of her two abductors.

The army have refused to release details of the operation, but it is understood the SAS unit scaled the cliffs below Mussenden Temple and surprised the kidnappers just minutes before four local men, including a 'Standard' reporter, arrived at the scene.

The SAS unit disappeared back to waiting boats in Lough Foyle after hearing the approach of the group, who had been tipped off that Danielle was being held at the Downhill monument.

The locals – Shay Gallagher MLA, Fr Noel Giddens, Ald. Tony Blunt and reporter Stan Stevenson – then found the bullet-ridden bodies of the two kidnappers, Rex Stovell and Wilbur Townslow, lying outside the temple.

Tony Blunt told the Standard: "We heard what we thought was thunder shortly before we arrived at the temple – we now know it was shooting.

"It was a terrible scene, one which no child should have to witness. But thank the Lord, she survived."

Danielle, who celebrated her tenth birthday only two days before she was snatched, escaped without any physical injury. But doctors say she remains too shocked to talk about the incident.

Channel

Mr Blunt confirmed that he had spent the previous week attempting to negotiate Danielle's safe release, using a "channel" he had opened up with the Loyalist Action Group some months ago.

After he had received a tip-off that Danielle was at Downhill, he contacted this reporter and Shay Gallagher, who is a close personal friend of the McEwan family. Assemblyman Gallagher then suggested that Fr Giddens should accompany them to the temple, as he has previously acted as mediator in several incidents involving terrorists.

When the four men arrived at Mussenden Temple, shortly before 10.00pm on Saturday, they saw no sign of the SAS unit. However, they did report hearing what sounded like two speedboats "having a race" on the Lough below.

The police, meanwhile, said last night that they believed Stovell and Townslow had been behind six murders in North Derry in the last five years – and had also been responsible for other serious crimes. They refused to comment on suggestions that the kidnappers could have been captured alive, other than to say that at all stages, they considered the two men to be "heavily armed and extremely dangerous".

(Further coverage and exclusive photographs of the carnage: Pages 2, 3, 4, 6 and 7.)

Stan also produced a clipping from page six of the Guardian, which reported the death of a war correspondent in Iraq:

NEWSMAN KILLED IN BAGHDAD

A senior reporter with ITN's Special Programmes Department was killed in a sniper attack in Baghdad on Monday afternoon.

Emile Rees, who was 41 and from Aldershot, was out shopping for a present for his new baby daughter, when a gunman opened up on a nearby US Marines' unit. Mr Rees had been due to fly home to see his daughter for the first time later that evening.

No-one else was injured.

Sue had bought in a couple of pre-release DVDs as a special treat for Danielle's return, so at about six o'clock we chased all the well-wishers and plonked her down in front of the TV, while we headed to the kitchen for a drink.

I then waited until Sue went to take a phone call before slipping into the living room to give Dee her new Nokia 3200. But it was all right. Even Mommy agreed she deserved it.

"By the way," said Sue later, as she kissed me goodnight and pointed me towards the spare room, "Stanley's report in the paper... It's complete bullshit, isn't it?"

•••••••

Of course, being a pessimist can have its good side as well in that, very occasionally, you get proved wrong. You spend your days expecting nothing from people, and now and again they surprise you.

Shay's courage put us all to shame. As soon as he heard they wanted him instead of Danielle, he agreed to hand himself over to Stovell and Townslow. And it wasn't false bravado either, like you see in young soldiers who don't know any better. Shay was really scared, but he stood up when it counted because he knew it was the right thing to do.

Tony Blunt was an eye-opener too. And despite all his born-again neuroses, he stuck rigidly to the story I gave them for the station. I made it clear to all of them: 90 percent of people are hanged out of their own mouths. When you're in the police interview room, say exactly what I tell you and not another word. Happily, they all did.

Audrey Grafton played bad cop with us just enough to make sure we understood that no holes had better appear below the official line. She'd been left to cope with three dead bodies that no-one could account for, and already she was being told to hide one of them. Stan, another revelation, squared a lot of her concerns with the piece in the paper.

And Sue was right, of course. The *Standard* report was complete bullshit.

AUGUST 2004

Shay wasn't the only one who'd been forced to step up to the crease. Against all my training and all my better instincts, I knew I had to get involved. If I'd left it to the rest of them, they'd only have fucked it up. So I put a rescue plan together along with Emile. I'd been able to contact him on a mobile number on the back of his 'ITN' card.

Tony Blunt had already established from a loyalist contact that there were only two of them holding Danielle and that they were hiding out between Downhill Forest and the ruins of the old house. So as soon as Shay got the call at the Stag's Head, all he had to do was send a text message to Emile to say exactly where the switch would be taking place.

Emile was already waiting in the forest, not far from the temple, along with Dexter Hart, Chris Caddle and Packie Naughton. And they quickly surrounded the site — a gun at every compass point, with Emile volunteering to cover the precarious cliff ledge.

Originally, I'd been tempted to let either Emile's people, or Chris Caddle's, take care of the entire rescue themselves, but Fr Noel had argued that it would have been little more than pre-planned murder. Besides, as Emile himself said, this way everyone was tied in.

I was directing operations from the high ground at Bishop's Gate behind the manor, so as soon as I saw Shay's car arrive at the front entrance, I gave the five-minute alert to the 'A-team' at the temple.

Fr Noel had stipulated, from the very off, that there should be no shooting and that Stovell and Townslow should be taken alive. So we promised. And we tried. Really. But then Townslow shot Emile.

•••••••

Friday, August 6

Tommy Bowtie knew I was going to put Sue in the picture, so he wasn't too sore when I admitted as much in Da Vinci's last night. I needed to talk about it as much as Sue needed to hear about it. I'd never seen a man die before, and all of a sudden, I'd got to see

115

three at once. "Bit like buses," sniffed Tommy, who is going directly to hell.

Things had been working to plan right up until Emile got shot. I walked up towards the temple about two steps ahead of Fr Noel, Stan and Tony Blunt. There was a little gate about 30 yards from the temple, and I climbed over it as instructed. Correction, I fell over it, I was so scared. The others remained just behind the barrier.

I was about halfway between the gate and the temple, when the door opened and Stovell appeared holding a pistol to Danielle's head. Up close, he was a scrawny little midget with buckteeth, the type who's always starting fights to prove himself.

"Let her go now, son," shouted Fr Noel from behind me. "You have Gallagher."

"Not until he's inside," shouted Stovell. And he gestured with his gun for me to hurry in. But as he did, there was a sudden barrage of six or seven shots at the back of the temple.

Emile, it seems, had noticed a small boat tied in a cove just below the cliffs. And as he was inching his way along the ledge, to cut the ropes that the kidnappers had left for their getaway, Townslow had spotted him and let rip.

"Gunman," yelled Townslow. "Abort! Abort! Abort!"

But it was too late. From a full 150 yards, Dexter Hart – who I later learned was a former Territorial Army marksman – shot Rex Stovell's throat out. And Chris Caddle was up and running like a thoroughbred towards the monument to settle the score for Aileen Bates. Townslow burst out through the window of the temple, Rambo-style, and loosed off a volley that could have taken out the lot of us. But he hit nothing but air. He then ran off along the cliffs. Fr Noel said he thought he saw Townslow's hands go up as Caddle gave chase. But Packie Naughton, who was nearest, swore that Townslow was actually attempting to fire his machine gun behind his head, when Chris killed him. The weapon then fell into the sea.

We did a partial mop-up at the scene, searching through pockets and the like, while Tommy Bowtie worked out our official stories. We were all to insist on him during questioning. The

A-team then disappeared, and we gave them five minutes before phoning Sue and the police.

Danielle, thankfully, had seen next to nothing. I'd grabbed her immediately after Stovell was shot, and Tony Blunt had leapt over the fence and thrown his jacket over her head. And yes, I'll admit, Blunt has his moments – and this was one of them.

"The problem, as you and I both know," said Tommy Bowtie last night, "is that, no matter what Fr Noel said, we couldn't bring them in. Stovell and Townslow knew too much. I mean, who could we bring them in to?"

I wasn't convinced, however, and Tommy knew it. I've spent the past fortnight trying to blank out the image of a man with no Adam's apple choking to death on his own blood at my feet.

"Look at it this way, Shay," said Tommy, "there were only two ropes down that cliff. And that little boat they had with them was only a two-seater. They weren't taking you home with them…"

Sunday, August 15

Both Sue and I had been recruited as independent observers to monitor yesterday's Apprentice Boys commemorations in the city, so we hooked up at my flat at eight bells. The morning march around the Walls was at nine, so we'd just time for a quick bite. (And a little breakfast as well.)

Thankfully, the march was largely hassle-free, so there was nothing to report. The best craic was actually standing on Bishop Street with the Derry Standard cameraman, Barry Magee, as the parade went past. Barry's unhappy that the PSNI have stalled plans to force officers to disclose their membership of the Loyal Orders. So every time he recognised a cop marching past in a band, Barry stepped out onto the road and took a close-up picture. He must have got around 20 before a duty cop worked out what he was doing and threatened to impound his camera as a security risk.

After giving the once-over to a full 15,000 Sons of Ulster, and suffering about as many versions of the Sash, I needed a drink. So I convinced Sue to join me in the Monico Bar just beside the Guildhall before she headed back home.

A tough old building the Guildhall. Ravaged by fire in the early 1900s, it was targeted a host of times during the recent conflict, before the natives finally adopted it as their own. My favourite story about it is how one of the guys said to have blown up the building in 1974 was asked one night at a table-quiz, what month in what year did the Guildhall last go up. "Fuck's sake," he'd replied, "do you want me to tell you if it was raining?"

I told Sue this tale as we sat drinking our Budweiser at a table beside the door, but typically she wasn't impressed. The bar was virtually empty because of the day that was in it. There mightn't have been any bother, but 'March Tourism' has a long way to go yet.

Despite several attempts, Sue declined my offer to stay over in Derry. She was worried Danielle might try and strong-arm Granny into taking her to a bonfire back home.

"Calm yourself, Shay," she laughed. "Besides, we'll have most of next week together at the Summer School."

So we had two drinks, and I left her to her car at Queen's Quay. We walked in silence. There was one very obvious matter she hadn't mentioned up until now, and I figured she was finally going to test me out.

"Something I have to ask you, Shay," she said as she opened the door of her Beamer. "When Dexter shot Stovell – what if he'd missed? How do you know Stovell wouldn't have killed Danielle?"

"Because," I said, looking full square in her eyes, "Tommy Bowtie had a full biography of Stovell thanks to MI5. And there's no way he was going to shoot his own daughter. Now was he?"

Friday, August 20

The Peadar O'Donnell Summer School in Glencolmcille is a lot less mainstream than the more celebrated Magill School but for my money attracts a nicer class of clientele. It helped big time that Sue and I were the only northern politicians there.

Sue gave a seminar on Tuesday on 'The Challenge for Young Unionism in a New Power-Sharing Coalition'. And despite the fact her talk was quite radical, the papers were only interested in the Q'n'A afterwards, which was all about the kidnap. Yes, she was terrified, yes, loyalist dissidents were still a threat, and yes, the abduction showed the two communities could work together to tackle important issues.

I took part in a discussion with a west of Ireland Sinn Féin councillor on 'Post-Ceasefire Nationalism: A Decade of Missed Chances?' the next day, but didn't have a lot to do. Last weekend's speculation that the IRA are preparing to disband had fired up the Sunday Independent politics unit, and they descended en bloc to give the hapless Shinner a good kicking.

I got a few slaps for "cowardly acquiescing to IRA total-itarianism" along the way. Overall, however, they went easy on me. Sue is the big dog's bollix with the Dublin 4 set at the moment, and they don't want her dented by association.

We spent last night in Teelin, about ten miles from the conference centre, in a little guesthouse exactly 200 steps from the counter of the Rusty Mackerel pub. The Guinness was too good to refuse, and the seisiún went on until the Guards threw us out.

It was a magnificent, warm night, so instead of heading to the B&B, we decided to stroll down to the pier about a mile away. By my reckoning, we were just about drunk enough to broach the subject, without being over the bar.

"One last question and I'll never ask again," I said to Sue as we sat on the harbour wall, holding hands. "Why didn't you tell me about Stovell?"

"Okay," she said, closing her eyes so she didn't have to look at me. "I'll explain it to you this once.

"Every day, Danielle gets lovelier and lovelier. She is a perfect little girl – my entire world. I would lay down my life a thousand times to make her happy.

"For the last ten years, all I've wanted to do was protect her. And the best way I could do that was to assure her that she was hugely loved and entirely wanted by everyone around her. So naturally, I was never going to tell her that her father was Ireland's number one hood. She knows her daddy wasn't a nice man and will never be part of her life. And that's more than enough for any child. Maybe in time I'll tell her more – but if I've the option I won't.

"The police had warned me that Stovell was obsessed with me. They told me that he would boast about being Danielle's father during interrogations – and even used it to suggest he'd political connections. One cop even asked me if I'd consider doing a blood test to rule him out. But I never would. I needed the deniability – for both myself and Danielle.

"I've no doubt that's why Stovell hated you so much. He couldn't handle the thought of a Fenian around the mother of his daughter. God forbid if Danielle were to have a little half-caste brother or sister."

We sat for a while saying nothing, staring out towards Muckross Head. A stiff breeze was starting to make its way in from the Atlantic just as the heat of the drink was wearing off.

"Want to go home?" I said.

"Sure," smiled Sue. "I've done enough talking."

We pulled on our jackets and walked back up towards the village in silence. As we got to the B&B, I held the door open for Sue, and as she went past me, she leaned forward and kissed me gently on the cheek.

"One more thing I will tell you," she said softly, "and it's one thing I'm totally sure of. If Danielle had got the chance to pick her daddy, Shay, it would have been you."

It was a beautiful moment. Magic even. A moment I'll remember all my life. But there was just one thing I had to check.

"Does that mean," I asked, "you'll let us chip the Cable again…?"

Sunday, August 22

Agnes volunteered to take Danielle to the flea markets in Belfast yesterday, so Sue and I headed back up to the Mussenden Temple. Sue was so happy to be out of the shop window for a few hours that she spent the journey up from Derry smiling fit to bust.

When we arrived at the Downhill Castle, Sue was cursing herself for not bringing a guidebook, but I told her not to worry. As soon as I figured that I could be getting to spend eternity on the estate, I'd studied up.

The short version is that the temple was built as a knocking-shop by Bishop Frederick Hervey on a remote cliff overlooking the north Atlantic. Hervey had the hots for his young cousin and built this 'library', modelled on a Roman temple of Vesta, just far enough from the main manor to keep his wife at bay. Tragically for the Reverend Fred, however, his cousin died before she got a chance to sample the scenery.

So Sue and I visited the temple and then looked round the remains of the great house half-a-mile away, which was in use right up until World War II as a British army billet. And afterwards, as it was a beautiful sunny afternoon, we sat on the cliffs looking out into the sea, wondering what to do next.

"So how do you know I'll never spill the beans on your big night out here?" she said eventually, with a flirty smirk.

"Well," I replied, "you gave me your word of honour as a Protestant. And besides, I saved your daughter's life."

"Nah," she laughed, "they'd never have shot her. I mean, thanks all the same, but it was you they were really after…"

"So what about your word as a Protestant?" I asked.

"I'd say it's about as good as your word as a Catholic, what do you reckon?"

"I reckon I'm in trouble, so."

It was time for my final card, so I took a deep breath and played it.

"There is another possibility," I began. "But it would only be as a complete last resort, mind. They say a wife can't testify against her husband…"

"Hmmm," she grinned, enjoying my pain. "We'll have to see about that."

She said nothing for about 30 seconds. Then a minute. Then another. Then another. Finally, she stopped smiling, took my hand and flicked her eyebrows over at the empty temple.

"Wanna go christen the bishop's knocking-shop?"

●●●●●●●

And they all lived happily ever after...

Don't put the mortgage on it. Though I'll grant you that even now, two months on, both Shay and Sue are still walking around with these big sappy smiles on their faces. That'll change when the fourth child comes around and Shay gets to spend a full year in the back bedroom.

Still, if he thinks he can be happy when no-one else can, good luck to him. But sure, the same fella reckons Stormount could be up and running by the New Year.

Like old Uncle Seamus once said, Shay's always been a big innocent sort of a bastard.